DNR

Do Not Resuscitate

Real Stories of Life, Death and

Somewhere In Between

by

Lauren Jodi Van Scoy, MD

This book is based on real medical scenarios. All names and identifying information have been changed to protect the privacy of the individuals.

This book may be purchased for educational, business or sales promotional use. For information please write: Special Markets Department, Pitkow Associates, 201 Welcome House Road, Perkasie, PA 18944.

Book and cover design by Michael Pitkow. Author's photography by Gabriel Fredericks.

Library of Congress Cataloging-in-Publication Data has been applied for.

ISBN 978-1-4507-6660-9 (softcover)

Dedication

To the memory of

Dianne Ball

Table of Contents

Introduction

DNR is not a book about death. Rather it is a book about the incredible stories of five people who, through their courage, conviction and spirit will serve as a glowing inspiration for patients and their families as they struggle with approaching mortality. DNR offers a window to the world in the intensive care unit by sharing the journeys of Bruce, Mrs. Chandler, Walter, Patrick and Victoria, all of whom are real patients with important stories to tell: stories of life, death and somewhere in-between.

As a young doctor working in a busy intensive care unit in a Philadelphia hospital, facing a family grieving at a bedside is the most challenging task my profession demands of me. Every day I find myself on the front lines of discussions with patients and their families about devastating illness, our fragile bodies and our inevitable mortality. It seems impossible for me to answer when a family asks me "what should I do?" Should they opt for aggressive, possibly painful interventions or perhaps allow their loved one to drift away? It's an impossible question to which I must give an impossible answer: it's up to you. As a doctor, I cannot make these decisions for my patients' families. All I have to offer is choice.

In the intensive care unit, we are faced with the sickest patients, often ones with chronic and incurable diseases that have begun to advance and rage beyond control. We resuscitate and stabilize, dodging bullets and saving lives for the moment, only to be left with another conundrum: now what?

And so I wrote DNR, a book that is meant to plant a seed in your mind about some of the medical situations you or your loved ones may one day face. I hope that DNR provides some insight for you and your family. It is with this spirit that I wrote the tales of five people with incredible stories, stories that kept me awake at night, begging to be written.

DNR

Do Not Resuscitate

Chapter 1: Bruce's Story

W HEN I FIRST met Bruce, I was overwhelmed by his vulnerability. His abdomen was exposed and a surgical vacuum dressing was all that lay between my hands and his organs. The 'vac', as we call it, was sucking out the infection, collecting the pus in a container that rested at his bedside. As I pressed on his abdomen I watched his face closely for a grimace to evaluate for any pain breaking through his artificially induced coma. He required heavy sedation to prevent him from fighting the ventilator and to make it more comfortable for the machine to do his breathing for him. I had to make sure we had the sedative levels just right. After all, I was an intern in the Cardiac Care Unit, and tonight, I was on call.

Bruce's daytime physicians explained to me before they left that Bruce's heart was failing and he had a large sternal wound from his last open heart surgery. He now had an infection, but not just any infection, The Infection, the resistant one. The one that was just as likely to kill him as it was for him to actually recover.

To enter his room I had to follow the typical isolation precautions, lest I transfer his super organism to another patient via my white coat. I washed my hands, put on the yellow isolation gown and gloves and I went in to get my lay of the land. All the alarms and beeps were as they should be. The drips were whirring softly on their pumps as they medicated Bruce to keep him alive. He had five bags in all: two were to keep his blood pressure from bottoming out, one was IV fluid, and two were the strongest antibiotics we had in our arsenal.

I had to take care of Bruce tonight; I was the front line. My seniors were just a phone call away, but somehow, that wasn't very reassuring. Bruce was hanging between life and death, and if he started to swing in the wrong direction, it was my job to pick it up- to notice. And so, there I was, covered in head to toe yellow isolation garb, checking things out- getting a 'baseline'. Some baseline, I thought. His blood pressure was teetering between Low and Very Low. His fever was a mere 101 and the ventilator was at its maximum settings. Truthfully, if things went downhill, there wasn't much more I could do, except notice... and watch.

I didn't think Bruce would ever open his eyes again. He'd never wake up. I didn't bother speaking to him–he couldn't hear me anyway, not through the drug-induced coma. I opened the packaging to a brand new plastic isolation stethoscope and placed it on his chest- his infection was too dangerous for me to risk contaminating my own stethoscope. I listened. There was a heartbeat. So far, so good. His lungs sounded crackly and the ventilator curves on the computer printout looked like a textbook. I glanced at the 'pus collection container' to make sure it hadn't suddenly filled with blood. It had about half a cup of ooze in it. The same it had been in the morning. Perfect.

Bruce's wall TV was turned to the local news and I stopped to check out the headlines. Someone should watch it, I thought. I stood next to Bruce for a few seconds and we watched TV together. The news was about yet another murder in West Philly and I was tired of the same story being on the news every night. I pulled the remote down from the bedside table, switched it to the hospital music channel, pulled off my gowns and went on to visit my next patient.

Bruce didn't die that night. Or the next night. In fact, he stayed in that state for the entire month I was rotating in that unit. He was what we call "a rock". You could pretty much find Bruce lingering between life and death at any given moment. But, other than that small detail, he was what we call "stable". I moved on to my next rotation, and then the next and if you had asked me, I would have bet on the fact that Bruce was dead.

In his younger days, Bruce was a self-proclaimed rebel. He was in and out of trouble as a youth and walked a delicate line where the law was concerned. His greatest pleasure was his motorcycle. He started with his first bike at age 15 and on it went from there. He started out with a moped and traded up to a bigger and bigger bike until he owned the largest bike there was. The roar of the engine matched his massive body and his muscular build. He'd ride anything and everything he could get his hands on. The Harleys, although he loved them, were just too small for Bruce. His bike was bigger, louder and stronger. You could hear him coming from miles away, and the vibrations were enough to send feeble ears screaming. The ladies would cap their hands over their ears as he rode through town and Bruce would flash them a quick smile of satisfaction.

Bruce's parents weren't quite as irked by his motorcycles as perhaps his neighbors were. Bruce knew that he wasn't exactly their 'golden child'. He saved that role for his brother, Joseph, the son his mother always wanted. Joseph was college bound and deeply religious in a way Bruce was not. It was always a struggle to get Bruce to go to church, but Joseph would go willingly and even spoke of studying religion once he was accepted to college. Bruce was well aware of the stark contrast between himself and Joseph but he also knew that his parents accepted him for who he was. And college was simply not on his list of priorities. He didn't have a life plan laid out, like Joseph, but he had a steady job at a local printing press and was always a responsible and reliable worker. The extent of Bruce's plan was to work hard and ride his bike into his future.

He met Sharon while they were both working the night shift at the press. It was on her first day that the boss introduced her to Bruce. After just one look, he had stuck out his hand and said, "Glad to meet you, will you go out with me?" Then 17, Sharon was taken aback and had to do some investigation about this Bruce character, but eventually agreed to go out on a date with Bruce after her coworkers gave her the thumbs up. Three weeks later, he walked her to her car after a late shift and asked her to marry him. She immediately said yes, surely raising some eyebrows in Small-town, Pennsylvania. 40 years and 4 kids later, I'd meet Sharon at the hospital as she sat at his bedside, having never left his side since.

At age 48, Bruce had his first heart attack and his first open heart surgery. The first time his chest was cut open, it was for a bypass operation. He dealt with it well and his recovery was rather uneventful. The docs had convinced him to get a defibrillator, a device that sits under the skin on a patient's chest wall that will deliver a shock if the heart goes into a deadly arrhythmia. He was back on his bike weeks later and he would ride to his monthly doctors visits.

It wasn't until Thanksgiving that things began to change. Bruce was sitting on the sofa, watching television, flanked by family members and his massive dogs. He felt a tickle in his hand where he held the remote. It was giving some kind of feedback as he was trying to turn up the volume on the football game and he quickly dropped it onto the sofa. His wife and kids looked over at him, giggling at how a little static electricity got Big Bruce in such a tizzy. But it wasn't the remote- it was his defibrillator- and they figured that out just as soon as the second shock rendered him unconscious.

Two weeks later, Bruce was lying in his hospital bed listening to Dr. Farber rattle off a bunch of words that didn't make a whole lot of sense. "Transplant list." "LVAD." "Bridge therapy." Sharon was, as always, by his side, looking equally dazed. They had gotten use to the word "CHF" or "congestive heart failure". They had gotten used to "heart disease". But the word transplant just didn't seem like something that was relevant.

Bruce didn't think he was that sick. He knew his heart was no good, but a transplant? It seemed impossible. But, like everything, Bruce shrugged it off and plugged away. He'd get on the list. He'd get a new heart. It would be no big deal. His denial would get him through it all and Sharon was right there with him. That was all he really needed anyway.

Dr. Farber's office ran like a well-oiled machine. She was one of the most highly celebrated heart failure doctors in the region and the LVAD surgery was something her office prepared their patients for routinely. They had case managers, nurse practitioners, cardiology fellows and medical residents. They had surgeons and psychiatrists, all ready to guide Bruce through the process.

But first, they had to explain. LVAD stands for "left ventricular assist device" and it is only placed in the direst of circumstances. The LVAD is a mechanical pump that supports the failing heart. It's a mechanical device that is implanted directly into the heart to boost its the pumping action. But its certainly no 'artificial heart' or miracle. The LVAD requires an external device to be worn, a machine, to which the patient is mercilessly dependent on. Tubes running from the machine to the LVAD open up avenues for infection, for blood clots, for bleeding and countless other deadly complications. The device is so complicated that they don't even teach you about it in medical school as its too daunting for medical students to truly grasp how it works. And Dr. Farber's office staff had to explain it to Bruce, and all their other patients, and make certain that they understood exactly what they were about to embark upon. For some patients, the LVAD is a bridge to transplant, meaning it is a temporary measure to sustain their life until a heart becomes available. For others, it is a destination- the end of the road. The last chance for survival. For those patients who aren't candidates for a heart transplant, it's the only alternative to death.

Dr. Farber reviewed Bruce's hospital chart, muttering to herself as she flipped through the pages. She scanned his numbers and thought to herself that Bruce was going to be a tough case all around the board. First, he had to overcome his lifestyle: he was overweight and a poorly controlled diabetic, a horrific combination for a transplant candidate. Second, she knew he was going to be waiting for a heart for a long, long time. Bruce's body habitus wasn't what one would call typical. In fact, not only would a suitable donor heart need to become available, but that heart had to be the correct size. It's not like picking from a catalogue, where you can order up a small, medium or large. No, Bruce would have to wait for an *extra* large donor of the right compatibility to die - and for that person to be an organ donor. If only Crate and Barrel made *that* catalogue. But Dr. Farber had been around the transplant block and had seen stranger things happen. She reviewed his prior echocardiograms and catheterizations and decided how best to medically manage Bruce while he waited for his precious donor heart.

Dr. Farber knew she had a job in front of her in getting Bruce ready for the LVAD. She had to get him stable enough so that his sick heart could endure the open-heart surgery to place the LVAD so he had a chance of making it until a transplant became available...if a transplant became available. She rounded on Bruce every day and tweaked his medical regimen daily, based on the severity of his shortness of breath and his labs. The office nutritionist counseled Bruce over and over about reducing his blood sugar and avoiding carbohydrate rich foods, but it took awhile to get Bruce to understand that his whole life needed to change. He was stubborn, rebellious, and incredibly tough. Dr. Farber knew he could do it; he just needed time to adjust. And he needed a good kick in the butt from his wife. And Sharon, Dr. Farber knew, would do just that.

After a few weeks in the hospital, it was time. Dr. Farber couldn't wait any longer. His symptoms were getting progressively worse and he was struggling to breathe. They had to put in the LVAD.

Bruce got his LVAD without much complication. He had met several other patients in his unit whose disease wasn't dissimilar from his own. He met Scott, another heart failure patient who had gotten his LVAD a year ago. Bruce met Scott in the CCU, and he was shocked at how sick he was. Bruce was thankful that he wasn't that sick, but talking with Scott and his family helped Bruce to understand what to expect with this new addition to his life. Scott told him all about the surgery, the recovery, and how the LVAD had affected his life. It was an incredible nuisance and uprooted Scott's life to the fullest extent, but it had given him a chance to get on the transplant list and to survive. Survive. That word was all Bruce needed to hear- he was signed up, signature on the "X". It was the second time they would crack open his chest, but he wasn't about to give in to his heart disease and he knew there wasn't very much choice in the matter. And maybe his course would be easier than poor Scott's. And so, Bruce got his LVAD without any problems and his cardiac rehabilitation began.

Although the surgery went well, the aftermath was less so. Since this was the second time that Bruce's chest had been opened, the healing process was a lot more difficult. Each day that his massive body lay on the bed, he was more prone to getting bedsores. Despite the nurses' constant attention in turning him from side to side, the bedsores still developed, and deepened. The pain was excruciating and the recovery was slow. But, eventually, Bruce made it out of the hospital. With his LVAD tacked to his side, Sharon took him home where his homecoming was celebrated by his family and two giant dogs.

At home, Bruce completely changed his diet and measured his blood sugar four times a day. Together with Sharon's cooking and his discipline, he was able to get control of his blood sugar. He worked tirelessly on his stationary bicycle and reported his progress to Dr. Farber at his weekly appointments. He monitored his blood pressure and his resting heart rate. His bedsores gradually began to heal. Eventually, he was able to live as normal of a life as he could, with the pump implanted in his chest and a machine strapped to his side. But Bruce was thankful that he was able to be active, to live, even if it meant being dependent on a machine.

Almost a year after his homecoming, Bruce began to notice a sound- a grinding. Something inside his chest was making a noise, something strange, something - not right. He called Dr. Farber's office and they made room for him in the afternoon clinic schedule. He sat on the exam table, afraid to move as Dr. Farber performed the electronics testing that would detect any problems with the LVAD. Bruce knew she would find something. He knew that his device was malfunctioning. He wasn't even sure if the grinding was a noise or a feeling, but he knew it was there when it shouldn't be.

Dr. Farber raised her eyebrows.

"It's working just fine, Bruce," she said. "The printout isn't detecting any abnormalities and your flows are holding up nicely." She looked at him as he sat, motionless. She hadn't seen him like this before- so alert and so silent. And somehow she knew that the computer must be wrong.

"We'll bring you in," she said "and watch you in the hospital overnight."

Bruce nodded and got down from the exam table. He had already packed his bag.

My friend and co-intern, Dr. Jason Tepian, took care of Bruce just as things started to go downhill. Jason had met Bruce months before I would rotate in the CCU, but he would tell me about his sickest patient over coffee breaks and late night calls. Jason was on Bruce's "primary team", which meant he was one of Bruce's daytime interns, not just taking care of him when on night call, like I did.

He was the intern who wrote the note on the chart every day, who followed every lab value, every fever, every heartbeat. He would report to the attending every day and together the team would make the plan for how to help Bruce to see tomorrow.

Jason would arrive every morning at 6am. The elevator would carry him and his coffee cup to the top floor of the hospital. He'd drop his bags off in the call room and set out down the hall for the CCU. The sliding doors would open and the CCU air would hit him in the face like a wet rag. This was his morning ritual and every day it was the same thing.

Bruce was in dire straights. He had been admitted a few weeks earlier after Dr. Farber brought him in for "observation" of his LVAD. It didn't take long for them to figure out what the problem was. The ball bearings in the device were grinding away and wearing down. The pump was breaking. Bruce had become incredibly short of breath, his legs swelled up like balloons, his blood pressure plummeted and he had been intubated and placed on the ventilator. It was just a matter of time before the LVAD would fail completely.

Jason wrote his daily progress note meticulously. The first line would say, "Pt sedated on ventilator. Unable to obtain history." The next few lines would record Bruce's vital signs and Bruce's painfully unchanging physical exam. Jason wrote the same thing every day. Next, he'd move on to the medication list, which easily had at least 20 different entries. And then, he'd write the plan. The Plan. Jason wasn't quite sure what to write. He copied his plan from the day before, changing it ever so slightly to comment on Bruce's urine output, his white count, and his temperature. He followed the therapeutic drug levels of the medications Bruce had on board, making sure they were at the right dose. Everything had to be perfect by 10am. That was the time the attending would come for rounds. Dr. Farber was the rounding attending today, and she demanded perfection. But Bruce's condition was far from perfect.

Medically, Bruce was in bad shape. Jason glanced over his notes from the day. He would have to present Bruce's case to Dr. Farber, knowing full well that Dr. Farber knew Bruce's story backwards and forwards. But, the role of the intern is to start with the same old phrase "This is a 54 year old man with past medical history of..." It was right around the word "past medical history" that Dr. Farber interrupted Jason, anxious to get on with the daily update.

"I know who he is, doctor," she said impatiently.

"Oh. Ok, do you not want a formal presentation?" Jason asked timidly. Some attendings wanted to hear the full report on rounds, and some just wanted to jump to the nitty gritty. Dr. Farber was more of a 'nitty gritty' type, and so Jason got to the point.

"His blood pressure has been dangerously low through the night. He hasn't been conscious much and his extremities are cold, so we don't think his circulation is holding up very well," he reported.

The team heard Dr. Farber swear under her breath. Everyone knew what it meant. The LVAD was failing. The heart wasn't pumping efficiently enough to keep the blood pressure up and his organs weren't getting enough oxygen without a strong blood flow. Bruce would have to be switched to a pneumatic driver, which is essentially a hand-crank, in comparison with the electronic portability of an LVAD. He would have to stay in the hospital until he got a transplant, if an organ became available before Bruce's current heart gave up.

Being an intern is a tough job and every day was a new challenge for Jason. He had to get blood and Bruce's poor veins had been stuck a zillion times over. He had to change IV lines. Some of Bruce's medications couldn't be put in through a regular IV. It had to run through a central line, a line that feeds directly into Bruce's diseased heart. This line was placed in through the neck, or near the clavicle, and it went down into the body about two inches until it fed directly to the vessels leading to the heart. The line is a portal to the bloodstream, a direct highway for dangerous bacteria to pass. The line had to be changed every seven days to prevent infection. So, every seven days, Jason stuck a huge needle into Bruce's chest to feed the new line into the heart.

Bruce eventually needed a feeding tube. He was on the ventilator. He was developing more wounds and infections from being in the same position for weeks at a time. The bedsores ran rampant. He required heavy sedatives and pain medications just to enable him to lie on his back. He had nothing going for him. And all of the interns secretly thought Dr. Farber should discuss with Bruce's family the possibility of converting Bruce's goals of care from aggressive to palliative care to spare him of the pain and medical torture we were imposing.

Jason would tell me daily updates about all the horrors poor Bruce would have to endure and we had many discussions about the fact that Bruce should be put on hospice, a service whose objective was to make patients comfortable and given a chance for a more dignified death. The suffering seemed to only prolong the inevitable fact that Bruce was dying. Jason and I talked about Sharon, and how the months of agony would be more than any single woman could take. But she continued to have hope when no one else seemed to. No one, except Dr. Farber, that is.

And then, it happened. One afternoon, Bruce's heart sighed and gave up. The nurse yelled out in panic when she saw the monitor. Within a second the crash cart was there and Jason began CPR. Fifteen people plummeted into the room all at once and the code began. The intensity level ramped up a million fold. Where there had once been the quiet buzzing of machines and soft beeps, there was now loud noises, shouting and chaos.

Jason's muscular arms could hardly compress Bruce's massive chest. He had to push against the chest wall hard enough so that the force of his hands would pump the heart. Bruce was already on the ventilator, so the lungs were taken care of. But they had to restart the heart. "Epi!" the cardiology fellow yelled as he came sprinting to the room. Luckily for Jason, the fellow had been nearby. The fellow was a lot more senior than Jason, and Jason was relieved to hear the fellow's voice calling for epinephrine. Jason didn't look up from the CPR. Sweat was dripping from his brow by this point and he didn't know what was happening around him, but he knew he had to keep the compressions going. He had to pump the heart.

"This is it," thought Jason. "No way will he come out of this."

But the code continued. The nurses skillfully obtained the blood samples. The fellow was masterfully running the code from the foot of the bed and the noise level was increasing exponentially. Jason looked up to catch a glance of the heart rhythm on the monitor.

"Hold CPR!" the fellow yelled above the chaos. Jason stopped, grateful for the rest.

"Check pulse!" was the next command. The monitor showed a flat line.

"No pulse!" a nurse responded from deep within the swarm of people working on Bruce.

"Continue CPR!" said the fellow. "And give atropine!"

And so it went for two more minutes. CPR continued. The IV bicarbonate went in, followed by the IV calcium. The nurses were scurrying around carrying out the orders as the cardiology fellow shouted them out. By now the medical students had all come in to catch some of the action. The eager ones stood behind Jason waiting for their chance to do *real* CPR. And they each had their chance. Jason and students took turns doing CPR.

"Hold CPR! Check pulse!" yelled the fellow. The medical student froze, not moving his hands out of CPR position.

"I have a pulse," said the nurse.

12

Jason's eyes shot to the monitor. He had a rhythm! Jason looked to the fellow, who despite it all was stoic and calm. He's got a pulse. He's got a rhythm. He's back from the dead.

Now what?

A little over a year later, I was back rotating in the CCU. I've never been a fan of cardiology, and going back to the CCU was not thrilling. But, it was my first day back, and I was now a senior resident in charge of an intern, so I was going to make the best of it. I printed out my patient list, and right at the top of the list was Bruce's name. Apparently, he was alive. I couldn't believe it. Had he been here this whole time? I could only imagine the state he must be in after all this time passed. I had heard about the code, but not much else. His chart must be on its 100th volume, I thought. Starting a new rotation with all new patients can be daunting, but especially when one of those patients is a rock, like Bruce. I find it easier sometimes to just head into the room and start, rather than paging through the unending pages of the chart. I needed a visual, something to get me started on updating myself and re-learning Bruce's case. I didn't bother to look in the chart; I needed to see *this* with my own eyes first.

I stopped outside his room at the isolation cart and gowned up with the familiar yellow gowns. The Infection, I remembered. I stepped into the room and almost fell over.

"Hiya doc!" Bruce said. He was sitting in a chair next to the window, eating breakfast and watching his television.

"Uh, hi" I said cautiously. "Are you Mr. Sellers?"

"The one and only," he responded.

I squinted my eyes to see more closely. It *was* him. Instead of seeing a horizontal patient, I saw a vertical man, sitting upright in a chair. He was strikingly tall and muscular, wearing a Harley Davidson T-shirt, which was quite a contrast to my 5 foot nothing, petite body. He had the typical 'biker' look to him, with brown eyes that were gentle, yet fierce. Replacing the ventilator tube that had been in his mouth was a smile that went ear from ear. If you saw him on the street you might think he was surly, but up close, he was a gentle giant. I couldn't believe that this was the man beneath the machines.

"You probably don't remember me, but I'm Dr. Van Scoy. I took care of you a year ago when you were, uh..." I hesitated, I didn't know quite how to say the words.

"Out of it?" Bruce finished for me.

"Yeah. Out of it," I said. I was kicking myself for not having read the chart before I walked in the room. I had no idea what was going on and I had no idea where to next take the conversation. I wasn't ready to do an evaluation on *this* person named Bruce, I was expected to see a comatose patient, the Bruce I remembered. So, I bailed out the way most residents do when they get into a situation where they don't quite know what to say: I plucked my pager off my hip and said "hang on, this thing is vibrating, I gotta go answer this. I'll be back."

"I'll be here!" Bruce said, spooning eggs into his mouth.

I made a beeline for his chart. I flipped it open and paged to the most recent progress note. "Healed sternal wound post transplant." No fever. No white count. No bacteria. No vac. The infection had actually cleared.

My first reaction was shock, and then an overwhelming guilt encased me. I had written him off as dead. I had thought how *cruel* it was that we were keeping him alive. That he had no chance. That he was a goner. I had thought he should have been a DNR. I had felt like we were wasting precious medical resources on a patient who had no chance for survival. I was ready to start the morphine drip. And I was wrong. Dead wrong. Because now, he was eating breakfast.

What kind of doctor was I anyway? How could my clinical judgment have been so off base? How many patients that I've put on hospice, how many that I've made DNR and started the drip...how many of *them* might have survived? Suddenly, everything I knew about end of life care and "death with dignity" was wrong. It was all flipped upside down. I had been disgusted by how aggressive we were being with Bruce's care way back when. Hadn't Jason and I had conversations about the fact that this patient was clearly not going to recover, that he clearly needed to be a DNR? And then, he had coded! And we had saved him. Why, I had wondered. For what? And now, it was very clear to me what we had saved him for. So that he could survive.

The revelation was terrifying. I knew what it meant. How would I ever feel comfortable making someone a DNR ever again? Could a doctor ever *really* know? Before, I had thought 'yes, the doctors know when enough is enough.' But now, I didn't know how I would face families looking to me for guidance, something that had come so easily to me before. The families will ask me for my perspective of the prognosis of their loved one and I would have to answer. If Bruce's family had asked me a year ago, I would have recommended DNR. I would have told them that we needed to make Bruce comfortable and maybe even withdraw care. How wrong I would have been.

Three days later, I strolled into Bruce's room. It had taken me several days to figure out exactly what had happened to Bruce during the last year. I had read his chart from cover to cover, shaking my head in disbelief. After his code, he had been stabilized and switched onto the pneumatic driver, the hand-pump of LVAD's. He had been plugged into that wall for months, only able to walk around the side of his bed. But, his heart continued to beat, and with each beat, he grew stronger. One spectacular night, the call came in. A heart was available. The surgeon popped his head into the room and said the magic words: "guess what!!?" Bruce recalled for me later the moment when he realized that he had a heart, and he insisted on doing one thing and one thing only: he would walk down to the operating room. The nurses tried to coax him onto the gurney, or at least into a wheelchair, but Bruce the Rebel knew that he could walk, and he walked his way right down into the OR with his surgeon by his side, awaiting the chance to open his chest for a third time in order to place the healthy heart. But after the third open-heart surgery, Bruce's sternum was angry and Bruce's body could not fight off the infection. His sternal wound took over 8 months to heal, and the infection ate away at his chest wall. He endured 8 months of dressing changes and antibiotics, of sedatives and pain medications, and against all odds, he beat The Infection.

"G'mornin!" I said. I was in a surprisingly good mood after reading Bruce's amazing chart.

A single large tear dripped from Bruce's eyes slicing my good mood. Seeing a tear come from this massive man caught me off guard. Had he been a little old lady with a tear, I would have sat on the edge of her bed and taken her hand, or perhaps placed my own hand on her shoulder to inquire what was wrong. Instead, I stood frozen and silent.

"What's wrong?" I asked him when I gathered my composure.

Bruce pulled himself together in a way that only a man can do and answered "I just found out information about my donor."

I kept quiet, waiting for him to continue on his own.

The Gift of Life, the organ donation agency, doesn't share personal information between donors and recipients unless both families agree, and even then, they divulge information very slowly. They have to be sensitive to both sides because after all, for every recipient saved, a donor must die.

"He was a biker," sniffed Bruce. "He died in a motorcycle accident."

I didn't know what to say. I had heard about the so-called biker brotherhood, but to see Bruce sobbing like this, I didn't know how to comfort him.

"Wow." I said. "How do you feel about that?" I was reverting to the textbook: ask open ended questions to illicit the patient's emotions. I didn't know if the technique would work on Bruce the Biker. But, it did.

"I don't know, Doc," he said. "I don't know. After everything I've been through, I don't even know how to thank him. All I do know, is that as soon as I get out of here, I'm going to get on my bike, I'm gonna rev' it hard, and I know I'm going to feel my heart smile."

Chapter Two: Mrs. Chandler's Story

I NTRACTABLE PAIN. I let out a sigh. They were my least two favorite words on a Monday morning, and my patient list was toppling over as it was. The last thing I needed was a patient whose complaint was intractable pain. The night shift resident, Ellen, whose shift was ending, was signing out the new patients to me and was explaining why Mrs. Chandler had been admitted, but I wasn't really listening. I was swearing in my head about the nightmare I had just inherited. She handed me the patient's chart and I muttered a quick 'thank you' as I spun on my heals to start off my day. First stop, the cafeteria. I needed coffee in a wicked way. No time to even print my patient list. I needed a caffeine fix to prepare me for my Monday morning.

I looked down at my feet as I waited for the elevator. Intractable pain, I heard the words turning over in my head. It was frustrating to have 'drug seeking' patients. At my hospital, it was all too common. They would beg for narcotics, to the point where they could barely keep their eyes open, yet were always seemingly able to wake up enough to ask for pain meds. It was frustrating, but part of the challenge was to distinguish who was drug seeking, and who was for real. Sometimes, it can be really hard to tell the difference.

The elevator opened with a "ding" and I stepped inside. It was jam packed with nurses, doctors and students, all heading for their own caffeine fix. We stood in silence as the elevator descended upon the 2nd floor cafeteria. I was the first to get out and as I quickened my pace to beat the masses to the coffee shop, my beeper went off. Irritated, I stopped at the house phone on the wall, watching as all the others passed in front of me for the coffee line. I dialed the number and waited.

"17th floor" a voice answered.

"Hi, this is Dr. Van Scoy, I'm returning a page."

"Hi LJ. It's John!" a voice quipped. John was my medical student.

Annoyed that he was making me miss my prime spot in the coffee line, I answered casually.

"Oh, hey, John, what's up?"

"I wanted to let you know that Mr. Smith's CT scan was normal," he told me.

I could tell he was proud to have the outcome of the CT scan before anyone else on the team had reported the result to me. He was one of the newer medical students, fresh out of the classroom and eager to be in the trenches. He didn't realize the night team had already told me.

"Oh, great!" I said, acting surprised, hoping it was convincing. The coffee line was getting longer by the second. "I'm gonna grab a cup of coffee and I'll meet you guys up on the 17th floor, ok?"

"Ok," he said. "I'll see you up here!"

I hung up the phone and stepped into the coffee line. It was going to be a long wait. I tried not to blame John. He was such a good student. He was eager, enthusiastic and incredibly bright. He was easily one of the best students in his class, so it was hard for me to really be annoyed.

My thoughts turned to my new patient on the 17th floor whom I hadn't even met yet but had already chalked up as being another narcotic seeking nightmare. The coffee line edged forward. Was I just cranky or was I really becoming jaded? Either way, it was nothing a little coffee couldn't cure.

I made my daily exchange of money for the paper cup and shuffled to the coffee dispensers with cup in hand. As I stirred in the milk, I began to plan out my morning in my head. As much as I didn't want to, I would go and see my new pain patient first. Now that I had my coffee I could start my day and by the time I got out of the elevator on the 17th floor, I felt like a new person.

"I saw Mrs. Chandler already!" John said as he saw me coming down the hall. "I can present her to you, if you want."

I smiled at John. The advantages of a good student were that they typically poured through the chart and could then present to the resident a nice succinct story.

"Great! Go ahead," I said, sipping from my cup.

"Ok, she's 88 years old and she has lung cancer. It's spread to her bones, all along her spine," he began. "She was apparently here a few weeks ago with a pneumonia and has been admitted here at least a dozen times in the last year for different infections and episodes of back pain."

I knew the story well. Lung cancer was a beast when it spread to the bones. It causes tremendous back and bone pain. If what John was reporting was correct, then this was no narcotic seeking patient, this was going to be much harder to deal with.

"OK," I said, "let's go see her together."

John led the way to Mrs. Chandler's room and I followed, slurping down the last of my coffee. I dumped the empty cup in the trashcan as we entered her room. A thin, frail woman lay before me on the hospital bed.

"Hi Mrs. Chandler," I began, "I'm Dr. Van Scoy and this is my medical student, John. We work with Dr. Simmons and we will be the team taking care of you here in the hospital."

"I need pain meds," Mrs. Chandler moaned.

I looked at my patient. She seemed to be swallowed by a sea of white hospital blankets and only her head popped out above the covers. She had prominent cheekbones (probably because her facial muscles had all wasted away) and her eyes were dark on her pale skin. She wore a grimace on her face and I could tell that her pain was real. At her bedside table was her untouched breakfast tray. I immediately felt bad for thinking she could be a 'drug-seeker'. Instead, I found this cute little lady that lay before me, writhing in pain. I would have to make it up to her.

"I'll check to see when the nurse last gave you your medication, and if its time for more, I'll have her bring it in to you. Have you eaten anything today?" I asked.

"No, I'm in too much pain," she answered.

"Ok, tell me where it hurts," I said, sitting on the edge of the bed.

"All over. I need pain meds!" she cried. I could tell she was not keen on answering my questions. I couldn't exactly blame her.

John shrugged at me when I glanced at him. It was obvious from the look he shot at me that he hadn't been able to gleam much information out of her either.

Just then, someone I had never met came crashing into the room. Her entrance made me instantly defensive.

"She needs her pain meds, miss!" the stranger shouted at me as she threw down her jacket and purse. I could tell she had just arrived at the hospital from the raindrops that still lined her coat.

"I'm sorry, who are you?" I asked, trying to be polite and hide my defensiveness.

"I'm Lisa, her daughter. Are you gonna just let my mother lie here in pain like that?"

I cringed inside. Accusations. I hated accusations. I had just arrived and uttered only one or two questions to my new patient and already the family was going to hurl hostility and accusations at me. Taken off guard, I was torn between my compassion for my patient and my immediate dislike of her daughter.

"Ok, I'm about to go get the nurse and have her give her some more IV morphine, m'aam," I said.

"Morphine doesn't help her pain," Lisa retorted.

"Well, I've only just met your mom. I need to review her chart and I'll speak with Dr. Simmons about changing up her pain regimen. I'll be back with Dr. Simmons in a little bit." I gave John the "let's go" look and left the room. I was annoyed that I had to abort the initial interview and physical exam with my new patient, but having Lisa there was going to be counterproductive, and I simply didn't have the patience for it. I'd send John in later to get the history and fill in the gaps. I knew John would love the opportunity to shine, and I decided to let him have his opportunity.

Three days later, I was sitting at the nurse's station looking at the daily labs for my sixteen patients. Disgruntled voices interrupted my train of thought and I glanced up from my computer to see Lisa gesticulating at the floor clerk. It was the same scene I'd seen every few hours over the last several days; Lisa was making a scene because the latest dose of pain medication was three minutes late. The clerk asked Lisa to wait in the room and told her that she would call the nurse. Lisa, surprisingly, obliged. Mrs. Chandler's nurse today was Jenny, and I motioned her over to where I was sitting.

"How much morphine are we giving her now?" I asked.

"Your intern changed it to Dilaudid, and she gets it every four hours" Jenny said.

"Do you think she is still in pain?" I asked. Being a nurse, Jenny had a much better understanding of pain levels than I did and I trusted her assessments. She was in the room many times a day, whereas I, as the doctor, would only go in the room for rounds and if there was a new problem. And truthfully, I avoided her room like the plague because of the "Lisa Factor."

"Honestly? No," Jenny said, "I really think she is fine now. When I turn her she has some pain, but overall, I think the Dilaudid is working much better than the morphine did."

Even though I was relieved to hear that the dilaudid was working, I knew it meant I'd have to go in and calm Lisa down. If the pain was controlled, I wasn't about to order more narcotics. I contemplated Lisa's behavior as I began my trek to the room. Why was she so aggressive and confrontational with us? Mrs. Chandler had cancer in her bones, and as sad as it was, she would probably never be pain free. Dr. Sara Simmons, Mrs. Chandler's cancer doctor, had countless conversations with Lisa about this sad truth but it just didn't seem to sink in. They didn't even want to consider hospice, which would focus on making Mrs. Chandler's end of life more comfortable and as pain free as possible. The objective of hospice was to control the pain as best as we could, walking a fine balance between under-treating Mrs. Chandler's pain and over sedating her with potent narcotics. Hospice agencies are experts in this arena. But Lisa expected the impossible- she wanted a restoration of her mom's pain free, cancer free life. And unfortunately, we just couldn't give her that. As I approached the room, I tried to prepare myself for the onslaught I was about to face.

I entered the room and was surprised to find it empty, except for Mrs. Chandler laying in her bed, with her mouth wide open and her eyes rolled up into her head. She looked dead and a shot of panic jolted through my body. My eyes darted to her chest and I saw that she was breathing, but her respirations were unnaturally slow. She had a lot of narcotics in her system and she looked groggy, but one thing was certain, she wasn't in extreme pain. She didn't look comfortable, but she certainly didn't look like she needed any more medication. I heard the toilet flush in Mrs. Chandler's bathroom and Lisa joined me at the bedside.

"Look at her!" Lisa exclaimed. "She looks awful,"

I took a deep breath and began. "I think she looks over-sedated, to be honest. I think we're giving her a lot of pain medications, which she needs, but we have to walk a very fine line here."

I saw Lisa's face begin to twitch in anger.

"Narcotics can suppress breathing, you see," I began to explain, "and although I don't think your mom is totally pain free, I don't feel comfortable giving her any more dilaudid right now. I don't want to sedate her so much that she stops breathing."

Lisa wasn't having it. "She looks like that because she's in pain!" she said.

I sighed. I was going to have to use 'the line'. I've used it before and although it made me uncomfortable to say, I knew Lisa needed to hear something dramatic.

"It's better for her to have a little pain than to be dead," I said, "and giving her too much pain medication could kill her. Look at how frail she is."

"I'm calling Dr. Simmons, then, if you won't give her any pain meds," Lisa threatened. Calling my attending was a trick she had learned recently as a way to punish me when I didn't do what she wanted.

"No problem. In fact, I'll go get her," I said as I left the room, happy for the excuse to leave.

Lisa was nodding enthusiastically as Dr. Simmons explained our new plan: an epidural. Not a cure, but a long term option for pain control while enabling us to decrease the amount of narcotics Mrs. Chandler required to keep her pain at bay. Lisa was clutching her hands together in excitement as Dr. Simmons explained the procedure.

24

"And once its in, we can taper her off the IV pain medications so hopefully she will wake up a little bit," Dr. Simmons finished. Lisa's eyes were bright and Mrs. Chandler was feebly nodding in agreement.

The following day, the pain medicine doctors placed the epidural and we began to reduce the narcotics. Everyone was on the same page. We had found a way to satisfy Lisa, but more importantly, we had a solid plan on how to deal with Mrs. Chandler's pain. I only hoped it would work. Time would tell, as epidurals can take a few days to take full effect. By the end of the week I left the hospital thinking that our problems would soon be solved and we could start the process of getting Mrs. Chandler ready for rehab. I'd have John call the physical therapists in the morning, the very first thing.

When I hit the floor the next morning, I was greeted by John. "Uh, LJ, can you come look at Mrs. Chandler?" he asked me, his voice a little unsteady.

"Sure, what's up?" I wasn't alarmed. John was a bit of an over-reactor.

"She's not looking good," John said.

"Ok, let's go see her," I said.

As we walked John filled me in. "She's just breathing funny and isn't making a lot of sense."

The only thing that surprised me was that it hadn't happened earlier. I didn't even need to evaluate her before giving John my first order. "Go get the Narcan," I said and he obediently bolted for the med room.

Narcan is a great drug. It can reverse even the most heavily sedated patient within just a few seconds. One push and an overly sedated patient would snap right back into reality. In fact, we use it as a verb: I was about to 'narcan' Mrs. Chandler.

When I reached the room, I did a quick assessment. Yep. She needed to be narcan'ed. Her eyes were rolled back into her head and she was breathing in long slow gasps. John and the nurse arrived a few moments later and the narcan was in the vein before I could even finish examining her.

"Mrs. Chandler?" I called.

She responded and looked up at me, a little confused as to why I was yelling at her. "How is your breathing?" I asked her.

"Fine," she said timidly. She was much more alert and her eyes focused on me as I spoke to her. The narcan had successfully awakened her, suggesting that her breathing had been slowed by an overdose of narcotics.

"Ok, good. I think you had a little too much pain medicine. Now that the epidural is in, we won't have to give you as much," I said. John was already attaching the pulse oximeter to her finger so that he could measure her oxygen levels. She was at 96%, which was pretty damn good considering how much cancer she had in her lungs.

A quick check of her blood pressure and pulse and I knew Mrs. Chandler would be ok. She had been getting IV fluids since the epidural had been placed, so I didn't expect her pressure would be low. It wasn't.

"Vitals every fifteen minutes and keep narcan at bedside," I instructed the nurse and as I left the room I added, "Keep an eye on her, John."

Six hours later, we had given Mrs. Chandler three more doses of narcan. Although each dose worked temporarily, narcan only lasts a few minutes and she would slip back into her state of 'la-la' land. But after 6 hours, the IV dilaudid had worn off and now I was beginning to suspect that something more than just narcotic overdose was causing Mrs. Chandler's breathing to worsen. I was waiting for the x-ray to come back. I suspected she might have fluid buildup in the lungs since she had been getting such a hefty dose of IV fluids. When her oxygen levels began to drop, I decided not to wait for the x-ray and give her the diuretic, hoping to speed up her urination enough to dry out her lungs.

"John," I said, "give Lisa a call," I was actually surprised Lisa hadn't visited yet today. "I have a bad feeling that Mrs. Chandler is taking a turn for the worse." As much as I hated to say it, I said "Tell Lisa she should come to the hospital."

John's eyes widened as he realized what I was saying. He was bright. He knew I was concerned that Mrs. Chandler was about to go into respiratory failure and that she would require the ventilator by the time the day was out. I gritted my teeth as I thought about the cancer load in Mrs. Chandler's lungs. If we put her on the ventilator, it would be near impossible to get her off again. Things were about to get a whole lot worse. Major decisions were looming and I braced myself for what was to come.

Dr. Simmons was yelling at me over the phone, "do NOT intubate this woman!"

She knew as well as I did that the outcome of this would not be good, but what choice did we have? We did not have an advance directive or living will and Mrs. Chandler was too sick to tell me what her wishes were. Certainly comfort care was the most reasonable option for someone as tragically ill and in as much pain as Mrs. Chandler. Prolonging her life artificially with machinery meant prolonging her inevitable decline, and probably also her suffering.

But, now, she was not able to make her own decisions and I had an irate family member on my hands. My job was to get Lisa to understand that her mom was dreadfully sick and that putting her on the ventilator was essentially the definition of finality. I had to go in armed with information and so I went to the break room to get a cup of coffee and gather my thoughts. I plopped myself down at the coffee table and drummed my fingers against its surface.

I knew Mrs. Chandler had an enormous amount of tumor in her lungs. I knew it had spread to her bones and was eroding her spine, causing tremendous pain. I knew that chemotherapy and radiation had not worked. I was confident that her deterioration was not solely because of narcotic overdose; it was also progression of her disease. I had seen her old x-rays with all her frequent pneumonias and fluid buildups. It wasn't hard to put two and two together: her lungs were tiring out and despite all her 'recoveries' from her previous pneumonias and all the narcotics we were giving her, it was just too much. Cancer was coming to claim Mrs. Chandler, and I had to make Lisa understand.

I stood up and headed for the x-ray viewer. My chest x-ray should have been back by now. I pulled up her name and reviewed the film. I was disappointed to see there was no fluid buildup to remove, no enormous pneumonia to treat...just cancer. This confirmed my suspicion that putting her on the ventilator was not a good option because her breathing problems were not temporary. They were permanent and the x-ray confirmed it. I saw John hang up the phone out of the corner of my eye. John nodded at me, telling me that Lisa was on her way.

When Lisa arrived, she was livid. The accusations began flying before I could even say a word. "You over sedated her! You put that epidural in and now she's not breathing! You need to FIX this! You need to fix my mom!"

My blood boiled. After all the demands for more medication, it took everything in me to keep myself calm and maintain my professionalism. I didn't want to have this conversation starting with this tone, but I didn't have much of a choice.

"Lisa, please calm down. Let's talk about what's happening and we can talk about what we're going to have to do next, ok?" I said, almost pleading with her. I placed my hand on Mrs. Chandler's leg to try to convey to Lisa that I truly did care about her mother.

I began. "First of all, I don't think your mom's deterioration is all due to the dilaudid." Lisa shot upright in her chair ready to let loose a mouthful, but I held up my hand to stop her. "I thought so at first, but over the course of the day I've given her several doses of a medication called Narcan, which reverses the effect of narcotics. Although it helped her a little bit in the beginning, it's not giving us much of an effect now and I think that something else is going on also. Her cancer is really taking a toll on her lungs."

"I don't want to hear about cancer," Lisa said. "I want you to fix my mom! You did this, you fix it!"

"Lisa, I'm trying to tell you I can't fix your mom, she is dying of cancer," I said, firmly, trying to keep the anger out of my tone. I knew Lisa was in denial and grieving but I had to maintain my composure and not let myself get emotional.

The conversation went around in circles for a few minutes and I began to get frustrated. I needed a new approach. I decided to show Lisa the x-ray. I brought her over to the nurse's station and allowed her to cross the invisible "no patients" line behind the main desk. The other nurses and residents sitting in the nurses station looked at me like I had six heads as I led the belligerent Lisa to the x-ray viewer. She was still yelling about how I had overdosed her with mother Dilaudid. I pulled up the film. The whited-out lung stared out at her. Lisa shrugged her shoulders.

"So?" she demanded.

"So, *this*," I emphasized while pointing to the whited out lung "is what is making her short of breath. Not dilaudid. Dilaudid doesn't do *this*," I said pointed at the screen. I was patronizing her and I knew it. I had a hard time holding back my anger now that I had an audience in my peers.

"I don't care about that," Lisa said pointing at the cancer. "She was breathing yesterday, does cancer happen overnight? No! It was something you did that stopped her from breathing."

"No, cancer doesn't happen overnight, but eventually, the disease progresses. All the evidence I have right now tells me that the disease is progressing and she has reached that critical point where her lungs can't take much more," I said. "There has to be a time when patients with end stage cancer deteriorate, and I think this is what is happening to your mom."

A stream of profanity erupted from Lisa's mouth. I was taken aback as I watched Lisa's body begin to sway from side to side as she shifted her weight. I suddenly became frightened that Lisa was going to turn violent. I felt threatened, so I took a step back.

"I'm going to have to ask you to leave the nurses station now," I said to her. I was uncomfortable that Lisa was now in 'my zone' behind the desk and I needed my space back. Showing her the x-ray had been completely ineffective and so I had to retreat. Lisa stormed off in a huff back to her mom's room and John took his place at my side.

"That's how you do it," I said, sarcastically. "I hope you were taking notes."

Back at Mrs. Chandler's bedside the nurses were watching her oxygen levels begin to drop. It was John that came to get me in the nurse's station where I had remained since the confrontation with Lisa.

"They need you," he said. "She's breathing at a rate of 35." A normal rate is 14.

I swore under my breath as I stood up. I was afraid to face Lisa again, but knew that I couldn't continue to have John as my representative in the room. He was just a student, and I was the doctor.

I walked in to see little Mrs. Chandler gasping for air. Lisa was on her cell phone, pacing on the other side of the room as the nurses were working to administer a new oxygen mask. "17th floor," she said into the phone. "Turn right off the elevator and she's in room 1795. The doctor is here."

I called for more diuretic and another dose of narcan as a last ditch effort to prevent an impending intubation. I looked into Mrs. Chandler's eyes and saw she was lucent.

"Mrs. Chandler, I'm right here. Listen, I need you to tell me if you want me to put you on a breathing machine if you need it to breathe," I said. She clutched my hand. "Lisa is here, too," I said, hoping the comment would soften Lisa up a little. "Do you want me to do that? Do you want to be on life support if you need it?"

She looked up at me but said nothing.

"My brother is coming," Lisa said. "He'll be here in a minute. He's on the elevator."

I didn't know there was a brother. Why didn't I know that? I didn't like being caught off guard and another interrogating family member was not what I needed just then.

"Sam is coming, Mom," Lisa said.

In the meantime, I ordered a few more labs and helped the nurses administer the medications I had ordered. It didn't take long before Sam arrived.

He entered the room and ran over to his mother. "She's so thin, Lis," he said. When Sam turned to me, I liked him immediately. He was stoic and calm amidst Lisa's chaotic persona. I was relieved to have a second family member to deal with. I went through the story with Sam, explaining to him as I had to Lisa. He nodded his head as I spoke, and unlike Lisa, didn't interrupt me. He asked me a few poignant questions about the timing of the epidural and the pain medications and pressed his lips together in thought.

"So, you and Lisa will have to make a decision about where we go from here. Do you know what your mom would have wanted regarding being put on life support?" I asked him.

"Mom wants to live!" Lisa answered.

31

Sam ignored her. "When we brought my mother to the emergency room, the doctors down there asked her what she would want if her heart were to stop, would she want to be resuscitated? Her answer was yes," Sam said.

"That's right!" Lisa contributed.

"Ok, well, we want to respect her wishes and I will call for a ventilator. But, I want you to understand that because her cancer is so end stage and so severe, it is unlikely that she will ever get off the ventilator once we put her on it. And it isn't going to fix her underlying problem," I said.

"She just needs it to rest for a few hours and then you can take it off," Lisa said.

Sam looked at me as if to ask if that was a possibility.

"Well, it doesn't really work that way," I replied. "Your mom's lungs would be dependent on the ventilator and although I can't say for certain that she would *never* get off the ventilator, I think it's a real possibility and I just want you to understand that."

"Get it," Lisa said.

Sam went over to his mom. "Mom, do you want the breathing machine? Do you?"

Mrs. Chandler didn't respond other than a few sobs. I watched as her heart rate was rising and I decided to call for anesthesia to come to the room, since once the decision was made, we wouldn't have a lot of time.

"Let's talk outside," Sam said to Lisa.

I was happy to hear that. I thought for sure Sam was foreseeing the complications of putting Mrs. Chandler on a breathing machine. He was such a contrast to Lisa, that I thought he would understand that there wasn't a cure. He would be the voice of reason. I had gotten through to him, I thought. He was my ally. Perhaps he could help me convince Lisa that the machine would not fix the cancer and would only make matters worse.

32

After a few minutes, they returned and Sam had a look of peace on his face. They had made a decision.

"Put the tube in," he said plainly, with his arm around Lisa. Surprisingly, seeing them arm in arm and united in a decision, even a decision I completely disagreed with, I was happy to oblige.

Dr. Roberts got the call about Mrs. Chandler about an hour after I had intubated her. He was lying in bed, reading yesterday's paper when his phone rang. He was the pulmonary and critical care attending and so he got the low-down from the fellow whom I had updated. Dr. Roberts' first and only thought was "oh, no." His years of experience told him what sort of mess was about to unfurl. He had been following Mrs. Chandler on the floor for her chronic shortness of breath, helping make recommendations to ease the symptoms resulting from the tumors in her lungs. But now, it was a whole other story. Lines, tubes, antibiotics, transfusions, infections, bleeds. She would get them all, he mused. The fellow, who I had briefed, had told him the family wanted everything done. Little old cancer-ridden Mrs. Chandler had about as much chance to survive this as a fish on dry land.

Dr. Roberts had come to accept death as a part of life, but it was the *way* she was going to die that bothered him. She was going to turn into a body kept alive by a series of machines. The cancer wouldn't make her heart stop completely and as for her lungs, well, the ventilator would do her breathing for her. If her kidneys failed, they could start dialysis. Modern medicine has the ability to do amazing things. We can keep people alive for extraordinary periods of time, but it always left Dr. Roberts wondering: just because we *can* do something, does it mean that we *should*? There wasn't much of a choice in Mrs. Chandler's case: she had voiced her wish in the emergency room to be resuscitated and her next of kin were requesting full and aggressive care. He listened as the fellow laid out the

33

plan, muttered a few "uh-huh's" in agreement, hung up the phone and let out a heavy sigh. Tomorrow was another day. Maybe the family would come around and realize that life support was not a good solution to someone with a terminal disease like cancer. Maybe. But if not, he had an arsenal of modern medicine, perched and ready to perform its 'magic'.

He thought back to his first meeting with Mrs. Chandler three months before I would come to intubate her. He had been consulted by Dr. Simmons to offer some specialty care for her increasing difficulty with breathing. He remembered seeing her in her hospital bed looking frail and old. She had a terrible functional status even then, being unable to get out of bed. Being put on the bedpan was a huge process in itself because of the tremendous pain she had when being moved and placed on the metal pan. It was pitiful to watch.

At that time, her cancer had caused significant amounts of pleural effusions, or fluid buildup, surrounding the lungs. To remove the fluid, he had performed a thoracocentesis or a "tap". A needle is inserted between the ribs and sucks out the fluid filling up the space around the lungs. Once the fluid was removed, Mrs. Chandler had felt significantly better. It was one small victory amidst her deadly disease. Lisa and Sam adored him for it, and their confidence in Dr. Roberts was sky-high.

"You really did it, Dr. Roberts!" Lisa had said snatching him into a huge hug, "You cured her effusions!" Dr. Roberts had been very uncomfortable with her choice of words as the word "cure" was not one he would use in the context of Mrs. Chandler.

He snapped himself back to the present, looked at his newspaper and threw it over the side of the bed. He thought about Lisa and Sam. From what he gathered from the fellow who updated him on the case, they were still going full speed ahead. It was a terrible situation: a woman with terribly end stage cancer, a poor functional status and intractable pain. There was nothing life support could offer her except prolongation of death. It was pretty rare for patients with this severe disease to end up on a vent, but when it happened, it was usually disastrous. It usually meant that the family wasn't able to let go and was unprepared for what was to come. Perhaps tomorrow they would have had more time to comprehend what was happening. He reached over to his bedside lamp, switched it off and flopped himself down on his pillow, waiting for sleep to take him into the next day.

Once Mrs. Chandler was transferred to the ICU, Dr. Hannah Griggs took over my role as the resident taking care of Mrs. Chandler. I was not envious of the job that awaited Hannah. The ICU rotation is hard enough with every fourth day being a 30-hour shift, but having a patient in as much pain and as end stage as Mrs. Chandler is tough. Add in a family in a state of denial about the disease process and, well, it's enough to run yourself ragged. I've had nights like Hannah was about to have, nights where you spent hours taking care of the medical maladies that arise one after the next throughout the night: first a low blood pressure, then a high potassium, then a low bicarbonate level, then another low blood pressure. It feels as though you are going around in circles, and by your 30th hour, your emotions run high and your patience runs low.

Mrs. Chandler's problem list grew longer and longer by the hour and Hannah was the resident who got each and every page. The first night Hannah met Mrs. Chandler was one of those long nights. Throughout the night, the situation grew more and more desperate. Her blood pressure had dropped significantly and she required medications called pressors just to maintain a safe blood pressure. Hannah was pouring fluid into Mrs. Chandler's veins and she was forced to max her out on three simultaneous pressor agents. Hannah thought for sure Mrs. Chandler was going to die.

Lisa and Sam were still vigilant by the bedside, and Hannah asked them to join her in the family conference room and so she could give them the most recent update.

Hannah could tell that Lisa and Sam were anxious to hear an update, so she wasted no time with pleasantries and began.

"I wish I had good news for you, but unfortunately things have gone downhill over the course of the night. Right now, your mom requires a lot of medication to keep her blood pressure up and her heart beating. Her lungs have completely failed and she is 100% dependent on the ventilator. We are doing everything we can to support her, but her body is systematically shutting down. I've also added some broad antibiotics, just in case she is brewing an infection that we aren't yet aware of, but most of her problems are resulting from respiratory failure at this point."

She paused to try and read their reactions. I had told Hannah about the confrontation with Lisa, so Hannah knew she had to be very careful with her wording, but she also felt obligated to be up front and completely honest with how dire she felt the situation was. She saw no reaction from Lisa or Sam and so she continued.

"I'm doing my best to get her through this, but I want to make sure I'm clear that I'm not hopeful that she can recover from this. I'm very concerned that her heart might stop tonight, and if that happens, I would have to perform CPR and possibly give her electric shocks if she has an arrhythmia. If that were to happen, we would compress her chest in order to physically push on her heart to keep it beating, sometimes causing ribs to break. Is this something you would want us to try if it got to that point?"

Hannah held her breath as she waited for the answer, but Lisa and Sam both vigorously nodded their heads 'yes'.

Hannah tried to hide her disapproval. All the CPR and shocks in the world would never save poor Mrs. Chandler. "Alright, that's what we will do then, but I want to make sure you understand that she is dying from her cancer and that I don't feel those interventions are going to make a difference in her outcome," Hannah said in a last ditch effort to change their minds.

"We understand she is sick right now," Sam finally said, "and we would like all measures to be taken to keep her alive. What you are calling cancer, we are calling overdose. It was the overdose that got her here. We will not discuss the fact that she happens to have cancer."

The room fell silent.

"Her body will fight. God will see to that," Sam said, breaking the silence. "Please continue to do everything you can. She is not going to die tonight. The Lord is with her and we will pray. She'll be just fine."

Hannah wasn't sure if he was trying to convince her or himself, but she could see that Sam was putting up a wall between himself and the reality of the situation. She understood how hard it must be to hear her words, but at least she had said them. She had said her peace, and excused herself to return to Mrs. Chandler's bedside. She had a lot to do and it was almost morning. Dr. Roberts would be in soon, and if Mrs. Chandler were still alive, she would have to be ready with a cohesive and organized battle plan for this impossible situation.

Once Dr. Robert's arrived the next morning, Hannah filled him in on the events of the last several hours including the meeting in the conference room. He went into her room and saw Mrs. Chandler's tiny body amidst the machinery. He glanced first at the monitor. Her blood pressure was extremely low, even on the pressors. He looked next to the IV drips to confirm the medications were as Hannah had reported.

Finally, he forced his eyes over to Mrs. Chandler herself, as devastating as it was to look. She looked even more cachetic than the last time he had seen her on her last admission, which he hadn't thought possible. She looked like a woman at the end of her line. The ventilator tube jutted out her mouth, with the strap clenched tightly around her jaw, indenting the lines into her face. Her clavicles protruded out from her chest wall like two lead pipes. Her eyes, sunken and dark, were only halfway closed, but looked like glass through the veil of the sedatives. He watched her chest rise and fall to the drum of the ventilator. The vent was alarming after every second or third breath, and he knew this was a sign that she was uncomfortable. She was "bucking the vent" as we call it. Her body was rejecting the machine's efforts and was trying to fight it, even through the sedatives. Dr. Roberts looked at the settings and made a few adjustments. As he did so, Lisa and Sam entered the room.

"Dr. Roberts!" Lisa exclaimed. "Look what they did to her!"

Dr. Roberts didn't know how to respond.

"Ever since they put in that tube, she has been a mess!" Sam added.

"This is typically what happens when someone as sick as your mom gets put on life support," Dr. Roberts explained. "It's not a benign process. The body undergoes quite a shock, and we usually try to avoid putting end stage cancer patients on life support for this very reason."

"But, she just needs a few days to rest her lungs and they'll take the tube out, right?" Lisa said.

"Well, its very unlikely, I'm afraid." Dr. Roberts said.

"We want to try," Lisa interrupted. "She was breathing fine yesterday, then they put in the epidural and whatever that did, it made her stop breathing. Once it wears off, we want her to get off the ventilator."

"One step at a time, Lisa. Let's first try to get her settled down on the ventilator. She is bucking against it and we need to fix the settings to fit her

38

body," Dr. Roberts said. He wasn't about to start the conversation about how useless this whole process was going to be. It was clear that Lisa and Sam wanted to push forward. He decided to set small goals for Lisa and Sam to focus on during what was to be a long process. He explained to them in detail about what it meant to be "bucking" the vent and that his first priority was to make her as comfortable as possible on the machine before even discussing any further plans. Lisa and Sam agreed and thanked him for his efforts to "make her better" and he left the room feeling defeated.

After a full week of making little to no headway in weaning Mrs. Chandler off the ventilator, Dr. Roberts and Hannah decided to have another family meeting to discuss the possibility of withdrawing life support and starting Mrs. Chandler on a morphine drip to ease her pain. According to Dr. Simmons, Mrs. Chandler was too sick to even attempt any further chemotherapy or radiation treatments, and so Dr. Roberts wanted to try and readdress the goals of care.

"You have *obviously* been talking to Dr. Simmons," Lisa said snidely to Dr. Roberts at the mention of turning off the machines. "We have no faith in her, you know, and now we have no faith in *you!*"

Dr. Roberts dropped his head. There wasn't much reasoning with Lisa. Every day that he had been seeing Mrs. Chandler he had been more and more pessimistic with his updates to Lisa and Sam in hopes of preparing them that things were going nowhere. She simply was not getting better. True, they had managed to keep her alive this long, but she was hanging on by the thinnest of threads. He hated inflicting suffering, but because Lisa insisted that they not sedate her completely with pain medications, he knew Mrs. Chandler was having pain and discomfort. It felt wrong to continue this woman's life in such an artificial and painful way. Mrs. Chandler's face would grimace with even the slightest touch, yet Lisa and Sam insisted that the pain medications and sedatives were the reason she was dependent on the ventilator. He had to get through to them, to explain that there was nothing medicine could do to restore her to the way she was, but neither Lisa nor Sam would believe him. He sincerely hoped that perhaps today they would be able to hear his words.

He had just finished a monologue about feeding tubes. Mrs. Chandler had no nutrition for over one week, but a surgery to place a feeding tube was not a good option for Mrs. Chandler. There is no evidence to support the notion that feeding tubes do anything to prolong the life of patients with end stage cancer. Especially when they are on life support.

"So you want to starve her to death?" Lisa said.

"She can't survive without nutrition," Sam agreed, looking blankly at his mother lying on the bed.

"She can't survive at all," Dr. Roberts answered. Hannah nodded in agreement.

With that, Lisa erupted in a stream of accusations, each more ludicrous to Dr. Roberts than the next. Lisa was screaming so loudly that the nurses in the next room began to cluster around the room to get a glimpse of the 'action'.

"Why aren't you getting her off the vent?" Lisa began, "why are you increasing her pain medicines? Why aren't you able to get the blood pressure up? Why are you giving her so much fluid? Why are the nurses only washing her once a day?" She fired them off like a machine gun.

Dr. Roberts' face began to get red as Lisa grilled him with more and more questions. With each question, he tried his best to answer.

"We're unable to wean her off the vent. We try every day but her vital signs become unstable as soon as we turn down the ventilator. We are giving her fluids to try and keep her blood pressure up so we can wean off the pressors. The fluids are also helping to keep her kidneys working. The nurses wash all patients once a day, that's our policy."

But no matter how Dr. Roberts answered Lisa's questions, she was dismissive of his answers and went on to the next accusation. Finally, Dr. Roberts had had enough.

"I can't talk to you anymore," he yelled back at her. "I've had enough!" He stormed out. He passed the nurses in the hallway staring in shock as Dr. Roberts shot out of the unit with a huff. This was completely uncharacteristic of Dr. Roberts, who was so tolerant and patient with families. Hannah and the nurses could only stand by and ponder what would happen next.

Hannah slid out of the room behind Dr. Roberts, whom she had never seen lose his temper before. She couldn't believe what had just happened. Lisa and Sam had already sworn off Dr. Simmons. If they weren't speaking with Dr. Simmons or Dr. Roberts, who *would* they speak to?

Dr. Roberts sat at his desk with his hands in his head. He was so angry he couldn't concentrate. His confrontation with Lisa and Sam was still ringing in his ears. He looked at the pile of papers in front of him and he tried to concentrate on being productive, but the conversation with Lisa and Sam wouldn't soften in his mind. It was 6:30 at night, and he had a long day. His wife was waiting for him at home and he longed to just throw on his winter coat and head home for a quiet meal. Instead, he picked up his white coat, put it on and headed back to the intensive care unit.

"I apologize for losing my temper," he said as he walked into the room. "That's not the way I am and I am truly sorry. Let's try and start over, from the beginning, because we need to find a common ground so we can help your mom."

Lisa remained silent.

"We're sorry too," Sam said. "We just don't want to hear that she is going to die and we are not ready to give up on her."

Sam and Lisa were the decision makers and Dr. Roberts knew he had to respect that. But as a doctor, he had to voice his concerns.

"We're not helping her, here," Dr. Roberts said after they had circled back to the feeding tube conversation, "and in fact, my concern is that we are hurting her. Putting in a feeding tube is going to subject her to an unnecessary surgery since she has virtually no chance for an extended survival."

"That's not for you to decide," Sam said respectfully. "That is not for you nor me to decide. Its up to God."

Dr. Roberts couldn't disagree with that.

"We want to give her a chance," Sam said, looking at Lisa. "We want the feeding tube."

"Ok, Sam. I'll call the surgeons first thing in the morning," he said, giving up. "Are we ok, now?" He was hopeful that at least the hostility was dwindling.

"Yes, doctor." Sam said. "Thank you very much."

And with that, Dr. Roberts was dismissed.

Ever since I had intubated Mrs. Chandler I had been visiting her daily in the unit and getting updates from Hannah. I wasn't Mrs. Chandler's resident physician anymore, Hannah was, but I still felt like Mrs. Chandler was my patient. I would pop down after rounds with Dr. Simmons and visit Mrs. Chandler to see what had become of her. Every time I'd walk into the unit, my eyes would race to the patient board to see if her name was still there. And it always surprised me to see that it was. I tried to time my visits for right before Lisa usually arrived since I didn't know how she would react to my visits. I hadn't seen her since the day of the intubation, but had heard of all the happenings from Hannah.

On my way down to the unit I ran into John, donning bright green scrubs.

"Hey, LJ!" he called to me.

"Hi, John. How have you been?" John had since moved on to his next rotation.

"I'm ok. I'm on OB/Gyn this month," he said, "I delivered my first baby yesterday!" His grin was ear to ear.

"Very cool!" I said. "I'm on my way to visit Mrs. Chandler, wanna come?"

His eyes narrowed. "She's still alive?"

"Yep. Barely," I added.

"Sure," John said with a shrug.

John chattered about his OB/Gyn rotation as we walked to the unit. When we arrived, John's chatter stopped abruptly. I realized that he had never been in the ICU and Mrs. Chandler's appearance came as quite a shock to him. All John's education and 'smarts' couldn't prepare him for the way she looked.

"She looks dead! She's... what happened?" he stuttered.

"She has terminal cancer and is on life support," I said sadly, "this is what happens."

John's eyes scoured over the bed, trying to make sense of what he was seeing. "Her arms are so swollen," he noticed.

"That's because her albumin is so low. Albumin is a protein that helps keep fluid from seeping out of her blood vessels and into her tissues, and since her cancer is so end stage, her body has devoured most of her albumin. Its not overtly dangerous, but it's a sign of a very poor nutritional state," I explained. "It upsets families tremendously though, for obvious reasons. But it's all just cosmetic."

"It's awful!" John said. He reached down to touch her arm. His fingerprint left a giant indentation in her skin. "It's like a soggy sponge!" John made a face of revulsion as he looked to Mrs. Chandler's legs. They were the same as the arms.

"It's not pretty," I agreed. "This is very typical, unfortunately, of people who go on life support for long periods of time and have really bad disease. I wish we could have avoided it. I don't know how Mrs. Chandler would have felt about this if she could see herself now."

John stood shaking his head. Mrs. Chandler's nurse, Kate, came in to the room.

"Hey, LJ," she said to me. She was used to my daily visits. "Do you think you can help me turn her? I have to put some ointment on her backside," Mrs. Chandler had apparently developed bedsores.

"Sure," I said. John looked at the clock on the wall. "I gotta go, I have a lecture in five minutes. See ya," He left the room.

"They always run for this part," Kate chuckled.

Kate and I turned Mrs. Chandler onto her side being careful not to dislodge any lines or tubes. My body twisted as I hugged her towards me and held my arms out to support the suspended tubing. The ventilator started alarming because of the sudden shift and my eyes glanced to Mrs. Chandler's monitor. Her heart rate had shot up. She was in pain, I thought, even through the drug-induced coma.

"Ok, just hold her there," Kate instructed, "it'll just be one second." She unpeeled the bandage that was taped to her bottom. A repulsive odor filled my nostrils and I grunted in disgust. "Yeah, it's bad," Kate agreed.

I held my breath as my arms ached from holding Mrs. Chandler on her side. Kate worked swiftly at applying the ointment and cleaning up the wound. I glanced down at the wound from where I was standing. It was deep. It oozed with a foul smelling purulence and I had to look away. Kate finished her work and we returned Mrs. Chandler to her position on her back. She bit down on her ventilator tube in a reflex. The whole process took about eight minutes and I was dizzy from holding my breath.

"Thanks," Kate said.

"Any time," I answered with a wave as I left to return to my daily rounds.

I wasn't at all surprised when I found out that the nurses had called in an ethics consult. The ethics committee was a panel of doctors, nurses, clergy and hospital administrators who responded to ethical dilemmas that arose in the hospital. Their purpose was one of checks and balances, to make sure that humane and ethical standards were carried out at all times in the hospital. If a situation arose where there may be deviation from these standards, an ethics consult could be called by anyone who felt it was needed.

It was Dr. Simmons who first told me about the ethics consult.

"The nurses called an ethics consult about Mrs. Chandler," she told me. "They felt like the family wasn't acting in the patient's best interest. The nurses said they feel like we are torturing Mrs. Chandler by keeping her alive when everyone knows she's never going to recover. I'm glad they called ethics, I've been saying we should do that for over a week!" Dr. Simmons said.

I knew Dr. Simmons had been hurt by how Lisa and Sam had turned against her. Dr. Simmons had a special place in her heart for Mrs. Chandler, who she had been treating for years at her office. I thought about how devastating it must be for Dr. Simmons to be the scapegoat for Lisa and Sam's anger about the cancer that was claiming their mother's life. Dr. Simmons had a close relationship with Mrs. Chandler before she had become the debilitated woman I met. I had no doubt that without Dr. Simmons' care and persistence, Mrs. Chandler would not have survived as long as she had. I was glad to hear that Dr. Simmons wasn't offended by the ethics consult and was instead embracing it.

"So, when is it going to be?" I asked.

"I think sometime today. I'll give you a page, if you'd like to come," she offered.

"Oh, definitely. I'll be there," I said. I just hoped nothing happened with any of my patients that would prohibit me from going. Planning ahead as a resident was almost impossible to do because you never know when the next fire would rage, needing to be put out.

Luckily, nothing came up, and I was able to make it down to the unit when Dr. Simmons paged me later that day. A cluster of familiar faces greeted me outside Mrs. Chandler's room. Several of the unit nurses, Dr. Simmons, Dr. Roberts and Hannah were all lingering in the nurses' station, waiting for the meeting to commence. Dr. Laramy, the assigned meeting chair, motioned us over to where he was standing at the entrance to the ICU conference room. We sauntered over to him and one by one streamed into the conference room. Dr. Laramy held the door open, as if granting admission. Dr. Simmons and I were the last two left to enter when he shut the door blocking Dr. Simmons' entry.

"Uh, Sara, the family just informed me that they don't want you to come to the meeting," Dr. Laramy said apologetically to Dr. Simmons. "We talked about it on the committee and decided that it's probably best for now if you don't come in. They have a lot of hostility towards you and I'm not sure how much progress we will be able to make with you there."

Dr. Simmons raised her eyebrows and tried not to show her shock. I could tell she was at a loss for words. I was rather shocked myself; I had been in several family meetings with angry relatives, but never had they prohibited one of the attending doctors from participating. This was certainly uncharted territory.

"That's fine," Dr. Simmons said, trying to hide her pain. I tried to meet her eyes but she had already turned and left. I followed Dr. Laramy into the room.

Lisa and Sam were seated at the conference table across from two women whom I recognized from the ethics committee, but whose names I didn't know. Two other women, apparently more family members, flanked Lisa and Sam. No one met our eyes as we entered. I wondered if they had seen Dr. Simmons being turned away.

The conference room was barren except for the rectangular table and its surrounding chairs. A sink and counter lined the back wall and the floor was lined with white tiling. The room felt more like a kitchen than a conference room and it probably had been at some point, but for now, it was the largest meeting room we had on the floor. As the doctors filed in the white coats blended into the background as they leaned against the wall behind the committee members seated at the table. I was the last one in and I fumbled with where to stand. There was a strong sense of "us versus them" in the room with the two sides aligned in a "face-off" position. I tried to maneuver myself so that I was standing at the edge of the table in an attempt to bridge the two groups into one large circle. The tension in the room was thick, and my adrenaline started to surge. I was surprised to find myself with butterflies in my stomach.

Dr. Laramy took his seat at the table, across from Lisa.

"I want to start out by having everyone introduce themselves and who they are, so we all know everyone who is present," Dr. Laramy began. "I'll start. I'm Dr. Laramy, I'm a nephrologist and the head of this ethics committee. As you know, some of the nurses who care very much for your mother have called the ethics committee as they felt that communication between the physicians and the family in this situation hasn't been going smoothly. Their hope was that having a third party mediation might help ease the situation. I also want to stress that I do not provide any medical care for your mom and I'm a third party, impartial member. I'm here to lead the meeting and address the concerns of both sides here."

I studied Lisa and Sam as Dr. Laramy made his speech. Both were sitting straight upright, arms folded across their chest. Their body language was defensive and I tried to read their faces. Sam wore no facial expression, while Lisa occasionally smacked her lips together, in what seemed like an effort to control her anger. Dr. Laramy, on the other hand, was sitting cross-legged in his chair with his hands wrapped around his knee. He looked casual, which I was certain was intentional. He was purposefully giving off body language to try and lighten the air in the room and although it failed miserably, I thought it was a nice attempt.

We then went around the room introducing ourselves one by one. There was myself, Dr. Roberts, Dr. Laramy, Kate the nurse, Bridget the case manager, Danielle and Joanna the ethics committee members, Hannah and of course, Lisa and Sam. The two family members that accompanied Lisa and Sam introduced themselves as Mrs. Chandler's granddaughter and niece. Danielle scribbled down the names of everyone present on her notepad; she was obviously also there to document and record the proceedings. I suddenly felt like I was on Court TV. The "us versus them" feeling was tangible and I could almost taste the bitterness in the air.

"Ok, now that we are all acquainted, I'd like to begin by having you tell me exactly what you understand about your mom's condition," Dr. Laramy began.

Lisa sat forward. "We want the breathing tube to come out," she erupted.

Here we go, I thought.

"No, before we talk about the breathing tube I want to know what you understand about your mom's disease and how we got to the breathing tube, just so we can all be on the same page," Dr. Laramy interjected.

Sam touched Lisa's arm to silence her. "She was getting a lot of pain medications on the 17th floor," Sam said, his voice was shaking. It was the first time I had seen him show any sign of nervousness. It caught me off guard to see him breaking down. It made me realize how incredibly stressful this situation must be for this unfortunate family. Here they were, medical laypersons without any form of scientific training having a meeting about their mother, whose care was completely in the hands of doctors that they simply didn't trust. I felt bad for them, sitting across from this army of white coats. It must be daunting. As angry as their continuous accusations about how the doctors were trying to 'kill' their mother by shutting off the machines made me, I also felt a new pity for them.

"She had gotten a lot of pain meds," Sam repeated "and so she needed the epidural to try and get her off the pain meds, but as soon as that epidural was placed, she went down hill." Lisa was rocking back and forth on her chair and nodding her head in agreement.

"They kept giving her more pain meds, though," Sam continued, "and she was like a zombie. I don't even know if she *was* in pain, you couldn't tell through all the drugs they had her on. She was so sedated and didn't make a lot of sense, so I don't know why they kept giving her more."

I felt adrenaline starting to surge in my veins, as he spoke, thinking of all the conversations I had had with Lisa about trying to limit the narcotics we were giving her while she was under my care. I glanced over at Hannah and saw her shift her weight in irritability. Our eyes met, silently communicating that we were both having a hard time biting our tongues. It was Sam and Lisa's turn to talk, and the purpose of this meeting wasn't to argue with them but to find a common ground. I was very aware of my anger causing my heart to accelerate in my chest and I looked to the ground in an attempt to calm myself.

The conversation went on for a few minutes about the pain medications. Dr. Laramy patiently allowed Lisa and Sam to vent their frustrations and I wondered if Dr. Laramy knew of Lisa's constant demands for more pain medications. It didn't matter if he did, but I had to fight the urge to defend myself, Dr. Simmons, and my team on the 17th floor as I listened to their accusations. I kept quiet, knowing defensiveness would be counterproductive.

"Ok, I understand what you're saying about all that," Dr. Laramy after awhile. "Let's talk about *why* she has pain to begin with. Let's talk about the cancer in her bones."

"No, we don't want to talk about cancer," Lisa said curtly. "We want to talk about getting her off the breathing tube." Sam nodded.

"With all due respect, we really cannot talk about one without talking about the other," Dr. Laramy began. "I understand that it's hard to talk about your mother's terminal disease, but it is central to this meeting, and therefore, I have to insist that we discuss it."

Lisa could see Dr. Laramy's firmness and knew they were not going to win this battle.

"Fine," she said, and she raised her arms up in a 'bring it on' gesture. "Let's talk about it. She has cancer. So what?" She placed her hands on her hips.

"Regardless of *why* she ended up on the vent, whether it be her cancer, narcotics or a combination of both, we still have to deal with the fact that she has terminal cancer. I'm going to ask Dr. Roberts to summarize his perspective on where she stands now, medically," Dr. Laramy turned to Dr. Roberts and gave him a quick nod.

"Well, it's not good at all," Dr. Roberts said. "She has an enormous amount of tumor in her lung and we have exhausted all our options for treating it. Her oncologist has told me that she wouldn't survive any more treatments of chemotherapy or radiation. Trying to shrink the tumor down is not an option. On top of the disease in her lungs, she is not maintaining her blood pressure on her own and she requires medications to keep her blood pressure up. Despite those pressors being at full dose, she is still having periods of low pressure, or hypotension. The hypotension is impacting her kidney function and her urine output is going down. All of these things are terrible prognostic signs."

Dr. Roberts paused. I glanced at Lisa, Sam and the family to see if I could find a glimpse of understanding in their eyes. The granddaughter's face was contorted as she held back tears, but other than her, their faces showed no sign of emotion or comprehension. If they did understand, I thought, they weren't going to admit it.

It was Sam who spoke up first. "We all understand that. But we have hope and faith."

Dr. Laramy turned again to Dr. Roberts. "Can you give us your opinion on what her chances of survival are, Dr. Roberts?"

"Well, I believe she unfortunately has a zero percent chance of surviving off the ventilator," he said quietly, but firmly. I saw Sam look over at Hannah who nodded in agreement.

"I don't believe in zero percent," said Sam. "Doctors are not in control and I have a strong faith that God will help her out of this."

Dr. Laramy leaned forward across the table to articulate his next point. "We aren't here to destroy your faith or hope, I want to make that very, very clear. We are here from a scientific perspective, and short of divine intervention, which I mean with the greatest respect, there is little hope that she is going to recover."

Silence filled the room which Dr. Laramy allowed to linger for a few moments before moving on.

After what seemed like an eternity, he finally broke the silence. "Let me change topics for a minute here. What do you think your mom would have wanted in this situation?"

"Mom wanted to live. She said so in the emergency room," Lisa said.

"The doctors came in and asked her if she would want to have shocks and CPR and stuff," Sam said, "and she said yes."

"Did she have a living will?" Dr. Laramy asked.

"A what?" Lisa said. Sam shrugged his shoulders.

"A living will, a document where she wrote down what her wishes would be," Dr. Laramy explained.

"No, she told us her wishes in the emergency room. She wanted to live," Lisa said.

These moments were key, and I knew it. Dr. Laramy was establishing Lisa and Sam's substitutive judgment. In the absence of an advanced directive or living will, Dr. Laramy would have to determine whether or not Lisa and Sam were making decisions based on whatever they understood Mrs. Chandler's wishes would have been had she been able to make them herself. This was the bare bones of the meeting, the reason we were all here.

"She said she wanted to be resuscitated while she was in the emergency room?" Dr. Laramy asked in confirmation.

"Yes," Lisa and Sam said in unison.

"Alright. That's a start. Now, did she ever discuss with you her wishes regarding long-term life support? Did she ever say she would or would not want to be kept alive on machines for a prolonged period of time?"

"Mom wanted to live!" Lisa said again.

"Yes, but would she want to live in the state she is now, do you think? It's an important distinction because saying she would want to be resuscitated if she had a hope of returning to an ends of a normal or even semi-normal state is quite different than what we are talking about here," Dr. Laramy said.

"We never asked her that specifically," Sam admitted.

"What do you *think* she would have wanted, Sam?" Dr. Laramy asked.

"I think my mother would have faith in God and that she would want to continue to fight until He took her," Sam responded. "That's what I think."

Religion in medicine has always been a mystery to me. The majority of my patients are deeply religious, but the way they interpret their religion can vary significantly. I puzzled over Sam's response. To Sam, 'letting God's will prevail' meant using science and medicine to its fullest and if she were to survive, it would be God's work. On the other hand, some patients feel that using science and medicine is working *against* God, and that if a patient is fated to survive, it has nothing to do with what we as doctors can do. Those patients chose to remove the machines and 'let God's will prevail'. Most patients I've encountered feel the latter and I continued to ponder over Sam's interpretation as the conversation continued.

"Lisa, do you agree with what Sam is saying?" Dr. Laramy asked.

"Definitely," she answered.

"Alright then. We've established that from the information we have, she would want to continue to be kept alive on life support," Dr. Laramy concluded.

Dr. Roberts raised his eyebrows. Hannah took in a deep breath. Danielle was scribbling furiously upon her notepad. The doctors were stoic. They all knew they had 'lost'. According to Mrs. Chandler's children, her next of kin and thus her legal decision makers, maintaining the patient's wishes meant going full speed ahead. Lisa and Sam didn't move. They hadn't yet realized the battle they had just won.

"So, we'll continue to do everything we can to keep her alive," Dr. Laramy said.

Now they got it. Grins from ear to ear stretched across their faces. Lisa grabbed for Sam's hand and they let out a few squeaks of joy. The granddaughter and niece put their arms around them in a congratulatory hug.

"So, where do we go from here, doctor?" Dr. Laramy asked turning to Dr. Roberts.

"The next step, I guess, would be a tracheostomy," Dr. Roberts said. "But we are going to have some trouble there."

"What's a tracheostomy?" Sam asked.

"It's a minor surgical procedure in which a surgeon will cut a whole in your mom's neck in order to place a more permanent ventilator," he began to explain.

"We just said we were going to try to get her off the machine! We don't want her to have a *permanent* ventilator!" Lisa exclaimed.

"If we are going to do everything we can to keep her alive, she needs to have a tracheostomy. First of all, the ventilator she has now goes down her throat and into her lungs. This puts her at great risk for getting pneumonias. After 14 days or so, all patients need to be converted to a tracheostomy. The tracheostomy is a hole in the neck through which we connect the ventilator, and it will hopefully make it easier for us to wean her off, if she ever gets to that point. This way, we can just disconnect the tube from her neck, and reattach it if she doesn't do well. With an oral ventilator like she has now, she would have to be reintubated if we remove the tube and she doesn't breathe on her own. Its much easier to wean someone if they have a tracheostomy, and much safer," he added.

"So, the tracheostomy will make it easier to wean her off the ventilator?" Sam repeated. He hadn't heard the word "surgery" or "permanent," he heard the word "wean." It was a theme with Lisa and Sam, I realized. They would pick and choose what words they would accept. Cancer, no. Overdose, yes. Permanent, no. Wean, yes. It was frustrating and I curled my toes under my shoes.

"If she stabilizes enough for us to try and wean her, then yes, it would make it easier," Dr. Roberts said.

"Let's do it, then. Can you do it tonight?" Lisa asked.

"That is what I was trying to explain before," Dr. Roberts said, a minor edge in his voice, "The problem is that no surgeon would do the procedure on her at this point. She is just too unstable. They would have to bring her down to the operating room, but right now, it's not safe to move her. We wouldn't want her to die in the elevator on the way down."

"So what do you have to do to get her more stable?" Lisa asked.

"Well, for starters, she would have to be off all pressors," Dr. Roberts said.

"She was off them for about an hour yesterday! Why didn't you do it then!" Lisa accused.

"She would have to be off them for longer than just an hour," Dr. Roberts said. "She would have to be off them completely for at least 24 hours before a surgeon would even consider doing the procedure."

"Ok, well, let's start moving the pressors down then. I saw the pump was at 15 today and it was at 20 yesterday, so they can probably bring it down some more," Lisa started, talking a mile a minute. "And her pain medication was being turned up too, I noticed. That one went from 5 to 6, and when it was at 5, her blood pressure was ok, so I think if they turn it back to 5 they might be able to fix her pressure! They just aren't trying hard enough!"

She was playing what I call "the numbers game." To play, all you need is an ill loved one and a feeling of helplessness. You come to the ICU for your daily visit usually to be greeted by someone who is non-communicative and comatose. You first arrive and walk up to the bedside. You might hold your loved one's hand. Then, you examine her face, with a quick kiss to the forehead. After you've said your "hellos" without any response at all, your eyes can't help but go to the monitor. There isn't much else to look at. By now, you know what a normal heart rate is and a normal blood pressure, and the monitor displays the numbers for you to see. Maybe the blood pressure is a little higher than it was yesterday, and it fills you with hope. Next, you examine the pumps and the IV drips, looking at the numbers on the drip poles. The sedation may have come down a little, and the pressors may have gone up. There may be a new drip running and maybe not. The ventilator has 10-15 different numbers on it, and over time, you realize that the number in the upper left is the percent of oxygen your loved one requires. The lower, the better. The doctors have told you that before. So, you can make an assessment based on the numbers you see. And you have an idea of what is going on. Down is good, up is bad. Being a doctor is so simple when you play the numbers game.

I've seen this game played often by my patients' family members and I could tell from Hannah's face that Lisa's 'numbers game' was wearing thin on her nerves. It's quite easy to get frustrated when family members try to micromanage their loved ones care and make requests about how we adjust the drips and ventilators. It's easy to lose your temper if you don't take into account the reason *why* they are watching the numbers. How helpless might *you* feel if your loved one can't move or can't talk to you? How would you feel if *all* you can do is watch their stillness? The only thing that changes is the drips and the monitors, so that is what they cling too. It's human. It's the need to help. It's the need to be there for your family member. Maybe it's guilt. But it almost certainly is love.

Trying to explain critical care and medicine to a family member who is playing the numbers game can wear on your nerves and test your patience. It's a skill I struggle with mastering. To not be angry. To not be defensive. To let them play the game so they can feel empowered. It's hard to do without losing your temper and it's even harder to know where to draw the line. Hannah had told me of her incredible frustrations with Lisa's 'numbers game'.

I looked over at Hannah who was gritting her teeth in the background. I knew that she was playing the situation over in her mind.

"Lisa," Dr. Laramy said kindly, "I think this is part of the reason why the physicians have been getting frustrated. You have to trust that they are trying to do what's best for your mom. Believe it or not, they *do* care. They *want* to help. We are all on the same team. They are going to do everything possible to help your mom, but you have to try and leave the medicine part to the doctors. I think it will help everyone communicate better if we can all establish a little trust and a little faith in each other."

Lisa sat back in her chair looking like a scolded child.

"He's right, Lis," Sam said, "We need to back off and let them do their job. We both do."

The words were shocking. Did he truly mean it? If he did, then maybe, just maybe things could get better.

"Ok," Lisa said after a period of time. "I'll cut the attitude. I just don't want to talk about shutting off the machines, anymore."

"That's fine," Dr. Roberts said. "We've established that we are going to continue going full force, but like Dr. Laramy said so eloquently, you have to trust us. We can't help your mom if there is no trust."

Lisa nodded, and for the first time, I saw that she understood and maybe even saw a glimpse of remorse. I could tell by the way her face changed, the way her eyes softened, that she was going to try to trust. My heart flooded with hope. Even though I personally felt that stopping aggressive care was the 'right' thing to do, I was pleased that finally, it looked like everyone was on the same page.

"We're going to try to wean down the pressors, and once we do, we'll attempt to get the tracheostomy in, ok?" Dr. Roberts said.

"Ok." Lisa said. She smiled broadly and then said "Thank you. Thank you so much."

Three days later, Mrs. Chandler's kidneys shut down and she was placed on continuous dialysis. When I walked into the room and saw the dialysis machine I knew it was an ominous sign. Things had gotten much much worse. The machine loomed large in the room, occupying almost half room. A labyrinth of tubes was coming off the machine's front panel, one of which was connected to a large catheter placed in Mrs. Chandler's groin. Blood from Mrs. Chandler's large groin vein (the femoral vein) was being sucked out of the catheter and snaked through the tubing into the medieval looking contraption. Whizzes, whirls and beeps filled the room. My eyes followed the blood as it was passed through the large filter on the dialysis machine. The filter serves as an artificial kidney by filtering toxins out of the blood stream in place of the failed kidneys. The blood that passes through the filter is detoxified and then fed back into the body through another port in the groin line making a continuous circuit.

Her soft, edematous body was a stark contrast to the enormous metal monstrosity that was sustaining her. Four enormous bags of fluid solution, called dialysate, hung above the machine and fed into the circuit so that the detoxification would work properly.

It was quite a sight to see Mrs. Chandler amidst the bags, tubes, machines and drips that surrounded her. She was so vulnerable and her eyes gaped up at the ceiling as her jaw hung open from the pressure of the ventilator tube in her mouth. She now required 8 IV drips, a feeding tube and 2 machines (the ventilator and the dialysis machine) to keep her body alive. I wondered about her spirit; was it still with us, or had it left long ago? What would she say if she could see herself from above? Was this truly what she meant in the emergency room when she told the doctors that she wanted to be resuscitated? There was no way to know and so her care pressed on.

Hannah's beeper went off around 1am and she groaned as she reached over from her call room bed to dial the number. It was Kate who answered on the other end.

"I think she is going to go soon. I haven't been able to keep her pressure above 60 systolic, and her body temperature is only 96 degrees Fahrenheit. I really don't think she is going to make it much longer. I think you should call the family in."

Once in the unit, Hannah looked into Mrs. Chandler's room. They had been through this before. Hannah had made the "I don't think she is going to make it much longer call" several times in the course of the last few weeks, but somehow Mrs. Chandler seemed to pull herself through. Sam insisted it was God, but it made Hannah wonder if God would be so cruel. She didn't want to start the whole ball rolling again, but when Kate had a 'hunch', Hannah trusted her judgment. She made the call.

While they were waiting for Lisa and Sam to arrive, Hannah helped Kate to change the padding underneath Mrs. Chandler's legs. Her skin was so edematous and soggy, that fluid was continuously seeping out of her pores. Her legs had blisters that were so fragile, even the most gentle of touches would make them burst. This was a result of her poor nutritional state, even despite the feeding tube. Kate knew that the edema upset Lisa and Sam tremendously, so she always made it a priority to change the pads.

As Hannah held Mrs. Chandler on her side while Kate changed the pads, she noticed that her fingers and toes were a dark shade of purple from a lack of blood flow to the digits. Hannah had noticed this the day before, but was shocked at how much darker the coloring had become in just 24 hours.

"Yikes!" she said, holding up her hand so Kate could see.

"Yeah, I know. Its been getting worse. Her toes have it too. They are black and necrotic," Kate said sadly.

"This is awful," Hannah said, "we can't even keep her pressure high enough to get blood into her fingers and toes."

"I know," Kate responded with a sad nod. Once the girls finished cleaning Mrs. Chandler they headed to the nursing station where they sat in silence, waiting for Lisa and Sam to arrive, feeling sad, helpless and defeated.

When Lisa and Sam arrived, Hannah was surprised at the relief she felt. She was glad they made it in time. Over the last one hour, Mrs. Chandler's blood pressure had been less than 50 systolic. It was just a matter of time before the heart would stop, and Hannah was thrilled when Lisa and Sam ran into the room while Mrs. Chandler's heart was still beating.

They swarmed to the head of her bed and kissed her head.

"We're here now, Mom. Hang on!" Lisa said.

Sam began praying as he held her necrotic hand.

"Her blood pressure has been very low for the last hour or so. The blood isn't getting to her organs, including her brain. The body can't sustain a low blood pressure like this for very long," Hannah said softly. Lisa and Sam had already seen the monitors and so Hannah didn't feel the need to belabor the point. She quietly left the room amidst their tears and prayers.

"Are we going to code her?" Kate asked outside the room.

"We are going to have to," Hannah answered with a shrug. "There's not much more we can do for her other than chest compressions though. We already have her on everything we can give her."

Just then, both Lisa and the telemetry monitor began screaming. Kate and Hannah stared at each other for a moment as if to say "here we go."

They stepped into the room as the other unit nurses came running with the code cart.

"I'm going to have to ask you to step outside now. We are going to code her," Hannah said to Lisa and Sam. Kate had already begun the chest compressions. Mrs. Chandler's tiny body was like an elastic band under the force of her compressions.

"Save her!" Lisa yelled, as another nurse pried Lisa and Sam away from the head of the bed.

"They will, Lis, don't worry," Sam said.

Once they were out of the room, Hannah turned to one of the other nurses that had come in to assist in the code.

"Epi, please," she said solemnly.

The nurse, Lacy, nodded and opened the code cart to prepare the drug. Kate continued the chest compressions and the room was remarkably silent.

"Epi in," Lacy said quietly.

"Continue compressions," said Hannah. She could hear Lisa and Sam sobbing directly outside the door. She was very aware to their presence and saw Lisa peeking into the room several times, no doubt to check on the fact that they were actually working on her.

Just then, a loud crack filled the air and Kate cringed.

"Someone take over," she gasped. She was tired from the compressions. "I just broke a rib."

"It happens," Hannah said, trying to reassure Kate that she hadn't done anything wrong. "You know CPR often breaks the ribs, especially in someone as frail as this. Don't worry about it. She didn't feel it. She's not there."

Kate nodded, but Hannah could tell she didn't feel any better. One of the other nurses had taken over the compressions and Kate stood by in silence, saddened by the crack she had heard and felt.

The code went on for 18 minutes. It was 18 long minutes to Hannah. Codes are usually chaotic and loud. They are filled with people shouting, needles flying and lines being placed emergently. There's always motion, noise and commotion. But this code was just the opposite. There wasn't much to be done. Dialysis had already been running for a week. They had plenty of lines and there was no need for new labs. The drips were all already running and other than chest compressions and the occasional epinephrine or atropine, there wasn't anything to reach for. Hannah alternated between epi and atropine and ran the code by the book. But the whole time, there was no pulse.

"Check for pulse," Hannah said again. She looked at the clock to see those 18 minutes.

"No pulse," the nurse replied.

61

"We've done three rounds of epi," Lacy said. She was keeping track of the medications on the flow sheet.

"I'm going to call it, but let me go talk to them first. Keep going," Hannah said as she left the room.

Lisa and Sam were right outside. They had heard everything.

"I'm going to stop the code now," Hannah said evenly. "She has no pulse and we can't continue to code her. She has been down for 18 minutes now, and the heart and brain are dead. Only the compressions are moving the blood through her body. I'm really very sorry."

"No, keep going! You haven't been trying long enough. You can't stop now," Sam said. Lisa was screaming through her tears.

"I'm sorry, Sam. But there is nothing I can do. I can't code her any more. She is gone," Hannah said firmly.

Lisa darted out the unit door and Sam followed her. Hannah watched as they went, feeling terrible for all that was happening. She returned to the room and instructed the nurses to stop the compressions.

The code ended and Hannah, Kate, Lacy and the others stood motionless looking at Mrs. Chandler. Her struggle was over. Kate reached over to turn off the dialysis machine and Lacy disconnected the IV drips from the lines. Just then, Sam and Lisa rushed in.

"She's not gone!" Sam said. "God is with her and he will bring her back to us!" He was almost hysterical.

Hannah knew what she had to do. She reached for the Doppler machine, which is a tiny ultrasound probe that accentuates sound so you can hear the heartbeat. She held it over Mrs. Chandler's carotid artery and turned up the volume. There was nothing but silence.

"Listen," she said softly. "There is no pulse. She has passed away and I'm really sorry. We're going to step out now and give you some time with her. Take as much time as you need." Hannah motioned to the nurses and they left the room, leaving Lisa, Sam and Mrs. Chandler alone.

As the other nurses scattered to return to their other patients and duties, Kate and Hannah sat in the nurses' station, waiting to see what would happen next. They heard the sobs and cries coming from the room and they could do nothing but sit and wait.

Kate began to write her nursing note about all that had transpired as Hannah paged her intern to get updates on the other patients in the unit. They went about their work with a heaviness and stoicism. The only sound was the drone of the machines, the beeps from the monitors and the sobs from Mrs. Chandler's room. No one spoke of the relief that it was over. No one said a word but could all feel that enormous weight had been lifted from the unit and tomorrow would be the beginning of a new day.

After a few hours, Hannah decided it was time to speak with Lisa and Sam. The sobs had softened then vanished completely over the last hour and Hannah knew it was time to ask Lisa and Sam about autopsy. They hadn't yet emerged from the room, but it was nearly 7 am and the paperwork needed to be completed. Legally, every family must be offered the opportunity for an autopsy to be performed on their deceased loved one. Hannah was certain that Lisa and Sam would want the autopsy. After all the accusations and all the suspicions, it was perhaps the only way they would get the answers they so desperately craved. Hannah was prepared. She was saddened by the thought of cutting open Mrs. Chandler's diseased body, but she also knew that it was probably the only way Lisa and Sam would ever achieve peace. Perhaps the autopsy information would give them some understanding that there was truly nothing more they could have done for their mother. Maybe they needed the autopsy report to help them understand the severity of her cancer. She only hoped it would help them move on and recover from their loss. Just one last intervention.

She entered the room and saw Lisa and Sam sitting by Mrs. Chandler, one on each side, holding her hands in unison. The stillness was overwhelming and she was briefly at a loss for words.

"Um, I need to ask you about autopsy," she stuttered.

Lisa looked up from her mother's face and met Hannah's eyes.

"No," she said immediately. "She's gone. There is no need. We don't need to make her suffer any more."

"Yeah, she has found peace and we don't need to do anything more," Sam agreed. "We've done all we can do. We want to let her rest."

"Alright, then. I'll be outside if you need anything," Hannah said. She was stunned yet heartened by their final decision. She was suddenly overwhelmed by affection for Lisa and Sam that she hadn't realized she had ever possessed. It was one that we all would come to know when looking back at our days spent taking care of Mrs. Chandler. We had come to know them, and even though they asked for the impossible, we still truly wanted to help them. It was anger balanced by compassion.

"Go ahead and rest, Mom," Hannah heard Lisa say as she left the room for the final time. "You've earned it."

We all have, Hannah thought, as she headed back to her call room to finally get some rest of her own.

Chapter Three: Patrick's Story

T ERRY BRACED HERSELF against the shower wall as she held her son in her
arms. His 19-year-old body was small and thin, but she still felt unsteady
supporting him as the water showered down on them both. She hadn't done this
in a long time; in fact, she couldn't even remember the last time Patrick had asked
her for help with bathing. But tonight, he simply wasn't strong enough to hold
himself up against the streaming water.

Terry held Patrick tightly, pushing her own body against the wall to prevent
herself from slipping. The air was steamy and Patrick was playing feebly with the
soap, trying to lather up his arms. His weakness was overwhelming and the
medications in his system were making him groggy and confused.

As Terry fought to maintain her balance, Patrick began hacking the all too
familiar cough. The humidity in the shower was loosening the mucus that pooled
in his lungs, so she held on tightly in preparation for the next coughing fit.
Patrick leaned forward and coughed so fiercely that Terry could practically feel the
pain in her own ribs. A huge gob of green nastiness spewed from his mouth, and
Terry closed her eyes to look away. More was coming and she didn't want to
see it.

Terry longed to be back on the sofa with Patrick where they had been just
hours before, watching movies and playing cards with his cousins. But instead,
she held him up, praying that she wouldn't drop him as his hacking erupted into
a massive fit. His body shook and Terry had to slide down to the ground as she

held Patrick; she simply could not hold him up any longer. Patrick sat at her feet, choking in air between his gasps.

And then, like a scene from a scary movie, a stream of green mucus spurted from deep within his lungs. Patrick wretched and shook, as he seemed to vomit up the sputum as Terry looked on in horror. It was endless and unlike anything Terry had ever seen. Having taken care of Patrick and his cystic fibrosis for the past 19 years, Terry was no stranger to mucus. But *this*, well, this was a whole different ballgame. This wasn't a half a cup, or even a cup. It was like a faucet had been turned on in her son's chest for which there was no off handle. She couldn't tell how much had come out now but Patrick wretched over and over, each time pouring fluid out of his sick lungs.

For the first time, Terry felt scared. She held Patrick tightly, unable to shake the images from the horror flicks he enjoyed so much. The stuff spewing from his mouth didn't look human to her and she never fathomed that so much *junk* could be pooling inside her little boy's lungs. She closed her eyes and prayed, waiting for the hacking to stop and for Patrick to be calm.

After a surreal eternity, Patrick finally stopped coughing and his breathing slowed to a calmer pace. It was over. Terry felt weak in her knees, but pulled herself together and reached forward to shut off the shower. Patrick remained seated, sobbing in the tub as Terry stepped out to get a towel for him.

While her back was turned, Patrick tried to pull himself up in the shower. She turned back just in time to see what he was doing, and shot her arms out to him just before he slumped into her outstretched arms. She wrapped the towel around him and embraced him, comforting him as she patted him down and held him close against her chest. Terry's memories raced back to the day she had brought him home from the hospital for the very first time, wrapped in his baby blanket, cooing as she had patted him, oblivious to the journey that two of them were about to embark upon.

Terry was still a child herself when Patrick's pediatrician, Dr. Cramer, first used the words "cystic fibrosis". She had delivered Patrick when she was only 17 years old and the thought that her baby could possibly be sick never even crossed her mind. But by the time he was 9 months old, Patrick had contracted pneumonia seven times, so it was no surprise to Terry when the doctors wanted to run some tests. Terry had gotten quite an education over the last nine months and so she knew the drill. When baby Patrick first came crashing into her life, she had no idea how much time she would be spending in doctors' offices, but she was used to it by now.

Dr. Cramer handed her a slip of paper that had the name of a pulmonologist scribbled on it, along with a series of lab tests. Dr. Cramer had already told Terry that he wanted to test Patrick for cystic fibrosis, but Terry had just blown off the idea. It was impossible that Patrick could have such a *bad* condition, so she hadn't entertained it as a possibility. She froze when she saw the test's name scribbled on the paper Dr. Cramer had just handed her. It read: "sweat chloride". It was two simple words, yet Terry knew that this was the answer. Patrick had cystic fibrosis, she was certain of it as the words of her mother echoed in her ears.

"Hand over my little salty-kins, Terry!" her mother would say, arms reaching out for her grandson. It was Terry and her mom's nickname for Patrick. He tasted salty when you'd kiss his baby soft skin, and the doctor was testing for sweat 'chloride'. Terry knew enough chemistry to know that salt was made of sodium chloride and the thought penetrated in her mind as she gaped at the words. Now that she knew Patrick had cystic fibrosis, she was afraid to ask the doctor what it *was*.

"Any questions?" Dr. Cramer asked.

Terry shook her head.

"Ok, well, I'll see you back after you've had the tests and met the pulmonologist," he said, smiling. He had no idea about "little salty-kins" or what was going on inside Terry's teenage head. Dr. Cramer left the room leaving Terry to stare at her child. Patrick was wiggling in his carrier and reaching for a stuffed shamrock. She handed him the toy and he bee-lined it directly into his mouth. As mother and son made their way out of the office, Terry knew her life would never be the same.

Terry was in the car driving towards Eastern Memorial Hospital for the trillionth time. She could have driven there with her eyes closed by now, she thought as she rolled down the window to let the night air blow onto her face. She had to make herself wake up. She was exhausted from her shift at the restaurant, but wanted to revitalize herself for Patrick's birthday celebration. It was his sixth birthday, and even though he was spending it in the hospital, Terry wanted to make sure it was a special one. She had bought him a new lego set last night after work and she couldn't wait to see his face when he saw it. Patrick was always building things, and when he'd finish one project, he would take it apart and start all over again. He loved puzzles, blocks and connect-sets and she thought he was sophisticated enough now to build the lego rocket ship that was neatly wrapped in the car seat next to her.

Terry reflected on the progress Patrick had made in the year since his last birthday. He was old enough now to understand that he wasn't like other kids, that he was sick and that he needed medicine. But he wasn't quite old enough to be angry or bitter. He knew that his friends didn't have to take pills or inhaler treatments but he was old enough not to be surprised when Terry sat him down for his hour-long nebulizer treatments. He would even sit still and wear the mask without a fight as it delivered the aerosolized medications. Well, most of the time. He no longer cried during the chest physical therapy, in which Terry would pound on his back to loosen the mucus that plugged his lungs. But despite his medications, inhalers and physical therapy, Patrick constantly developed upper respiratory tract infections requiring antibiotics, some of which needed to be taken three or four times per day. But he was at that perfect age, Terry thought, when he was too young to feel any sort of bitterness, but old enough to be cooperative.

As Terry drove, she thought about the resilience of her youngest child. She thought about how easy it was for him to keep up with his older brother, even though he was two years older and healthy. Patrick could run and play like nobody's business, and even his hospitalizations didn't slow him down a bit. She had learned so much in the last six years. When Patrick had first exploded into her life she hadn't even heard about the disease 'cystic fibrosis' but now, she felt like an expert. After the shock and confusion had passed, she devoted herself to making sure that life went on, and now, six years later she was continuing to do just that. For a disease that had once been such an enigma to her, she realized now that she couldn't imagine life without it. After all, it had come from her and, therefore, it was a part of her.

Patrick's disease was genetic, inherited when two parents each possess a hidden mutant gene that can be passed silently through generations. If that mutant gene is passed on by each parent to the child, then that child is afflicted with cystic fibrosis. The gene codes for a special protein called a "chloride channel" which allows special ions to pass through the tissues of the lung's airways. Without properly functioning chloride channels, the mucus in the airway becomes dangerously thick, making it difficult to clear secretions and clogging up important glands in the lungs, pancreas and liver. The thick, stagnant mucus serves as a source of dangerous infections which plague those afflicted with cystic fibrosis. The doctors had taught Terry how to administer chest physical therapy to Patrick, which was a painful process in which Terry had to thump on

Patrick's back to help break up the thick mucus plugs in his airways. It was hard hitting her own child so forcefully, but she had to do it, no matter how much they both hated it.

Over the years, Patrick had adjusted well to his frequent hospitalizations. In fact, these days Patrick thought there could be nothing better to being in the hospital. The children's ward was colorful and filled with all kinds of toys and activities. Patrick had all day to play, except when he had to return to his room to receive his treatments. But the rest of the time, it was like a tornado of fun. There were video games, puzzles and movies. There were board games, art projects and best of all, plenty of other children to play with. Patrick was a social kid and he loved spending time with the other kids in the hospital, whether they were his age or not. His days in the hospital could be spent building models and flying paper airplanes. In between activities he would eat ice cream and other goodies. It was a six year old's bliss.

Terry turned into the hospital parking lot and after a few rounds of circling, she slipped her Volvo into a spot, grabbed Patrick's birthday package, and headed into the hospital. Once inside, she flashed her visitor's pass from the night before at the security guard, who smiled and waved her through the glass double doors leading into the pediatric ward. Even though Patrick had only been admitted twice this year, the security guards still recognized her as she came in.

She entered the hallway and gave a quick wave to Theresa, Patrick's nurse from the night before.

"Hi, Theresa," Terry said as she passed.

"Hi Terry! He did great today! He let me give him all five treatments!" Theresa called back.

"Oh, great! Thank you!" Terry replied as she turned the corner to the corridor where Patrick's room was. She was really anxious to see him and didn't feel like chit chatting. After all, she trusted the nurses by now and knew that they were taking good care of her baby.

"Mom!" Patrick called as he saw her from inside his room.

"Hiya birthday boy!" Terry said.

"Dad gave me a toy truck!" Patrick said, delighted. Gary was Patrick's stepfather, but had essentially raised him since Patrick was 2. Patrick's biologic father had left before Patrick had even been born, which was just as well for Terry. She had plenty of other things to worry about. Not only did she have Patrick to take care of, but she was also a mom to Gary's two other children, Seth and Kara. Seth was two years older than Patrick and Kara was about Patrick's age. Seth and Kara were fantastic kids, but still required a lot of attention and love. Terry had to make sure that she paid equal attention to her "sick kid" and her "healthy kids". It was a lot to take on and there were days were she felt so overwhelmed she could barely breathe. But today wasn't one of them.

"A truck, eh?" Terry said, planting a quick kiss on Patrick's forehead.

"Hi, honey," Gary said, after Terry said her hellos to Patrick.

"Hi," she replied as they exchanged a quick kiss.

"How was work?" Gary asked.

"The same. Good tips today though," Terry answered. She turned towards Patrick, holding his gift behind her back.

"What is it?" Patrick squealed.

"Open it and see. I think you're gonna like it!" she teased with a musical cadence.

Patrick was tearing into the paper almost as soon as Terry revealed the package to him. Terry took a step back and reclined into Gary's arms. He gave her a soft squeeze.

"A lego rocket ship!" Patrick exclaimed, "I wanted this so bad! Seth said I probably can't build it, but I bet I can!"

Terry and Gary spent the next hour by Patrick's side, happy to see him so joyful even though his breathing had worsened in the last few weeks. He had another infection and his pulmonary function tests had gotten low enough that his doctors felt that he needed IV antibiotics and more aggressive nebulizer treatments. But despite being hospitalized, Patrick was upbeat and energetic; it amazed Terry that he could remain so 'healthy' despite being so 'sick'.

"Ok, well, I'm going to go pick up Seth and Kara from soccer practice now that Mom's here," Gary told Patrick.

"Ok, Dad," Patrick replied, not looking up from the lego box.

"I'll see you at home, honey," Gary told Terry.

"Sure," Terry answered, "I'll be home in a few hours. You can heat up the leftovers from last night for Seth and Kara, ok?"

"Ok," Gary said and gave Patrick a kiss and Terry a wave and he was out the door. Terry and Gary had to tag team often to keep the family running smoothly. Between the two of them there was always somewhere to be, someone to pick up or some activity to attend.

"Seth and Kara aren't coming?" Patrick asked.

"Not tonight. They're going to come tomorrow after school, but they have to finish their homework once they get home since it's a school night. But we're going to have a big birthday cake when they come tomorrow night and Grandmom is going to come too," Terry answered, hoping that Patrick wasn't too disappointed that she didn't arrange for his brother and sister to be with him on his birthday.

"Ok," he said nonchalantly. Terry was watching his face for any signs of disappointment and as she studied his face, he suddenly let out a yelp so suddenly that it made her jump. She tensed up for a split second but then relaxed as she realized that Patrick's yell was one of excitement as he had just pulled out the directions for his new lego rocket ship.

"This is awesome!" he exclaimed and then erupted into a coughing fit from his sudden outburst of excitement. He began hacking loud, fitful gasps and Terry watched as his face turned beat red from the episode.

Theresa, the nurse, came rushing in upon hearing his distress and once she saw Terry's relaxed face and Sean's legos spilled out over his bed sheets, she immediately understood what had triggered his attack. She smirked and put her stethoscope to his chest.

"Oooh, a wheezy birthday boy! I'll get you a treatment and we'll have you fixed up in no time," she said, reaching for the tubing and facemask at his bed stand.

Patrick continued coughing and concentrated hard on controlling his breathing.

"Just a...short one..." Patrick let out between coughs. "I want to build the...the ship!"

"First things first, Patrick. Take your treatment," Terry said.

Theresa attached the container that held the liquid medication to the bottom of the facemask. The mask fit snuggly around Patrick's nose and mouth and she tracked the tubing to the wall machine that would convert the liquid medication into an aerosolized nebulizer treatment for Patrick to inhale. The medication would help decrease the amount of bronchospasm that was occurring in his lungs and would calm the wheezing he was experiencing. These treatments worked fast and after fifteen minutes or so, Patrick would be back to his regular self. But Patrick flopped back in bed, breathing slowly into the mask with a pout on his face from his impatience. Terry tossed him a sympathetic look understanding that Patrick's six-year-old brain was yearning to play with his new toy, but knowing that for now, his legos would have to wait.

As each year passed, Patrick became more and more resistant to taking his treatments. After school, Patrick, his brother and the neighborhood kids would dump their backpacks in their respective houses and then meet up in the street for whatever the 'game of the day' was. Some days it was baseball, some days soccer, and some days it would be video games. Whatever the game was, it began the instant their feet hit the pavement as they hopped off the bus and lasted until dinnertime. They'd race to their houses to see who would be back to play first, but Patrick would always lose.

"Patrick, take your treatment first!" Terry yelled back as she hurried to the hallway to intercept the boys as they dropped off their schoolbags. If she didn't get there soon enough, 8-year-old Patrick would be out the door again before she could blink.

"Awww, Mom! Can't I do it later?" Patrick whined.

"*Later* is time for the *next* treatment," she said sternly as Seth slipped out the door en route to Jon's house.

"You never let me do anything fun and I always have to stay in and get treatments and I really don't care if I die. I'm going!" Patrick shouted and stormed out after his brother leaving Terry speechless in the hallway.

It was the beginning of a perpetual argument that would last for years to come. It was always Patrick versus Mom or Doctors versus Patrick. As he got older, he had less and less patience for his nebulizers and Terry began to lose control as Patrick ascertained his own individuality. It began with testing. He'd skip the afternoon treatment and test Terry every day after school to see just how far he could go. He tested and tested her and Terry grew more and more weary. She was, after all, a mother faced with an impossible situation. It was either fight with her child every day with the *hope* that maybe the treatments would prolong Patrick's inevitably shortened life at the expense of him missing out on play- or she could allow him to skip his treatments and just be a kid.

74

As Patrick grew from 9 to 10 to 12 years of age, Terry struggled with the daily battle. He wouldn't listen to her. He wouldn't listen to his doctors. In fact, he barely paid attention during his visits with his pediatric pulmonologist. He would fiddle with whatever action figure or toy he'd brought along, breath into the lung function machine at the doctor's request and promptly return to his toy. Terry's frustration and fears grew day by day. She'd toss and turn at night pondering over Patrick's pre-pubescent mind and his deadly chronic disease. She saw more and more how Patrick craved normality, he wanted to be like the other kids, free to play when he wanted, and eat without requiring medicine first. As he got older the hospitals became less fun and more of a nuisance to him, and it was painful for Terry to watch the transformation.

Having a child with a chronic disease is hard enough and often parents take the brunt of it. Terry had no problem with that. She was an achiever, a fighter. She did what she had to do. She had the support of her husband and her mother and she had her bond with Patrick. But now, that was beginning to shrivel before her very eyes. She and Patrick fought more than they talked. Patrick shouted more than he laughed and Terry hated her role as the enforcer.

Over time, Patrick and Terry began deal making. As he wore her down, she would allow him to skip the after school treatments as long as he promised to allow her to perform his chest physical therapy before bed and get in three treatments a day, as opposed to the five that were prescribed by his doctors. It wasn't ideal, but Terry had made her decision. She was going to allow Patrick to be a kid, and as long as he maintained a moderate level of compliance with his regimen, she would have to be satisfied. All she wanted was for her child to be happy and healthy, and if he couldn't be healthy, she at least wanted him to be happy for whatever time he was going to be with her in this life.

By the time Patrick was 12 years old, he began managing his own disease. He took ownership of his cystic fibrosis and showed an understanding way beyond his years. Terry noticed him paying more attention to his doctors and even asking questions at his visits.

"How come you keep giving me different antibiotics?" Patrick asked Dr. Hammond, his pulmonologist, as he prescribed an antibiotic Patrick hadn't taken before.

His question took Terry aback. She actually had been about to ask Dr. Hammond the exact same question, and her heart swelled with pride at her son's intelligent question.

"Well, if I keep giving you the same antibiotic over and over again, then the bacteria in your lungs might get used to it," Dr. Hammond explained. "This way, we're constantly exposing them to new drugs so they won't build up a resistance."

Patrick nodded thoughtfully. He had a concerned look on his face that didn't go unnoticed. Both Terry and Dr. Hammond watched as Patrick prepared his next question.

"What is the cystic fibrosis superbug?" Patrick asked quietly, "I heard someone talking about it last time I was in the hospital. They said its what kills people with cystic fibrosis. Do I have it?"

Dr. Hammond spread a gentle smile across his lips. "No, Patrick. You don't have it. The infection is called 'cepacia'. It's a special bacteria that commonly infects patients with cystic fibrosis and its incredibly resistant to antibiotics. That's why they call it the 'superbug'. It can't be killed, kind of like superman. But you're right, it's very serious and we are trying to prevent you from becoming infected with it. Normal people can fight off *cepacia* if they inhale it, but in people with cystic fibrosis, it can be deadly. But you don't have to worry about the right now, ok? Your cultures are showing *pseudomonas* infections mostly, and that's why I keep changing the antibiotics. I don't want the *pseudomonas* to become resistant too."

Patrick jerked his head in a quick nod and looked over to Terry. It was clear he wanted to change the subject. It was at that moment that Terry knew Patrick understood how serious his disease was. Although he was just a kid, he was also a kid faced with grown up problems and Terry realized just how mature he actually was.

It was after that doctor's appointment that Terry began treating Patrick like a teenager when it came to his decision-making. She had no doubt that Patrick could handle it. He was smart and responsible and he knew the cost of his choices. The fighting lessened and their relationship blossomed with a mutual trust and respect. Gone were the days of arguing. Terry let Patrick skip his afternoon treatments, and didn't have to hassle him as much about taking his three daily treatments. They were becoming less like mother and son, and more like friends.

By 14 years of age Patrick had moved from building legos to a "taking things apart" phase. He loved to work with his hands and was curious about the way things worked. It wasn't unusual for Terry and Gary to come home from work to find Patrick wrapped up in a tussle of wires, cords and circuit boards. Remote controlled toys were his new favorites and after steering (or flying) his latest gadget around the house for a day or so, he would disassemble it and then reassemble it back to fully functioning order. But that wasn't always enough for Patrick. Once he was finished mastering all his own toys, he'd move on to his sister's toys, much to her dismay.

Whenever Gary would bring home a new appliance or gadget, Patrick would insist on putting it together all by himself. He would carefully pull out the instruction manual and study the diagrams like an architect over a blueprint. And then, he'd dive right in, head first, to whatever the task at hand. Gary would sit back and supervise Patrick, lending a hand only if Patrick asked for help, which he seldom did. He never needed it. He was bright and extremely good at what he did. If he saw a picture of something, he could build it without ever reading the manual, just by looking at the pictures.

But Gary and Terry soon began to realize that Patrick's skill at understanding pictures and diagrams was a mere adaptation. The truth was that Patrick was fourteen and he could barely read. Physically, Patrick was on par with the other kids his age. His disease made him skinnier and more frail than the other kids, but he was more than able to keep up with them. When Terry would watch Patrick run and play with the neighborhood kids, she'd often worry that he just might snap in two. But he never did. Coddling Patrick was not her style and she had made a conscious effort not to hold him back from all the rough boyhood play.

But when it came to reading, Patrick was *way* behind. Terry and Gary soon realized that his lengthy hospital stays were beginning to take a toll on Patrick's schoolwork. He was lagging behind the other kids, although he was well adapted at covering up his deficits. It was only if you really paid attention that you realize Patrick's reading and writing skills were inadequate for his age. After all, since childhood he had been in the hospital at least two to three times a year, and now in his early teens, those numbers were rising to more like five or six times a year, and each hospitalization seemed to get longer than the next.

When he did go to school, he would have to leave class two or three times per day to go to the nurses office to receive his nebulizer treatments and medications, thereby missing up to an hour of class. He'd also have to leave ten minutes before the lunch period began so that he could take his pancreatic enzymes he required to properly digest his lunch. It seemed Patrick was out of class more than he was present and his grades began to suffer.

But despite all of this, Patrick was one of the most popular kids at school. He was well liked by all his teachers and peers and had a very active social life. He had tons of friends and was always surrounded by his best buddies and giggling girls. In fact, Shawna, a pretty 14 year old girl, was coming over quite a bit those days, and it didn't take Terry long to figure out they were a couple. And so when Terry made the difficult decision to pull him out of school, it was met with quite a bit of disdain.

"What? Why?" Patrick yelled, exasperated when Terry told him that she had hired a private tutor.

"Honey, I know its not easy, but I've had a lot of discussions with your teachers and we all agree that its just too much for you to keep up with class and be in and out for your treatments. Its just not a good situation for you," she tried to explain.

"But what about my friends? What about Shawna?" Patrick asked, tears now welling up in his eyes.

"What about them?" Terry answered. "They will still be your friends. Shawna will still be able to come over. And we've already arranged with the school that you can participate in all the clubs and after school activities you'd like."

Patrick was silent as he thought this through, eyes down to the ground. Maybe this wasn't such a terrible thing: no classes, but clubs and sports. Terry could see the gears turning in his young mind.

"Let me think about it," Patrick said.

"Alright, we can talk about it again after dinner," Terry answered, but the decision had already been made.

By his mid-teens, Patrick's life was preoccupied with two things: fixing up cars and Shawna. Shawna and Patrick spent hours together, him fixing up her old car, and her watching him as she proudly passed the tools as he called for them. Terry liked Shawna a great deal. She was academic and did quite well in school. She was highly organized, which Terry thought was a good influence on Patrick, who was quite the opposite. Shawna walked a straight edge, and would scold Patrick if he went out drinking with his older friends. Yep, Terry liked Shawna a *lot*. She even brought her along with them on family vacations. Shawna and Patrick were like two peas in a pod; they were a perfect blend.

When they were both 16, Terry and Gary took all the kids on a Caribbean vacation. Terry, Gary, Kara, Seth, Patrick and Shawna were one big happy family as they jetted to the Bahamas to escape the bitter cold of Pennsylvania. It was during that vacation that Patrick had forgotten to pack his nebulizer. Once they reached the hotel room Terry realized that Patrick was without his nebulizer bag, she felt a rage build up in the pit of her stomach. How could he forget something like his nebulizer? How could he be so irresponsible? She had trusted him to pack on his own bags and now she felt completely betrayed. Patrick could see the anger in his mother's eyes.

"Calm down, Mom. Let me talk to you about it, ok?" Patrick said, glancing over at Shawna, who nudged him on, as if she knew what he was about to say.

Terry waited for Patrick to speak.

"I purposely left the nebulizer at home," he began.

"What!?" Terry said, dumbfounded at his statement.

"Relax, Mom. We are only here for three days and I just really wanted three days without any treatments. Just three days to be normal. I brought all my other medications, but I just don't want to miss out on the Bahamas by being cooped up in the room with my nebulizer," he hedged searching Terry's eyes for some kind of response. When she said nothing, he continued.

"Don't be mad. Shawna and I have been talking about my cystic fibrosis a lot, and we've decided that I can't continue to be the 'boy in the bubble'. If I'm going to be alive, I want to live. I know I'm not going to live much past my twenties. I know that and so do you. So while I can, I want to enjoy myself. I want my life to be about living and not only about my disease. I'd rather live to be 20 on my terms than to be 30 without experiencing life. I just want to be normal. And while we're here on vacation I want to be on vacation from my cystic fibrosis too, ok?" his voice trailed off as he saw tears pooling on his mother's eyelids.

Terry wiped the corner of her eye with her index finger. The tears broke loose and streamed down her cheeks.

"I'm so proud of you, Patrick," she managed to squeak out while holding back her sobs and also her fears. She embraced him tightly and as he held her back, she felt his tense body loosen in her arms. It was then that she realized how fearful Patrick must have been to tell her what was weighing on his heart. She clenched her eyes tightly as they embraced, and when she opened her eyes, she saw Shawna standing beside her, tears welled up in her eyes as well with a sympathetic smile across her face as her eyes locked on Terry's.

Patrick let go of his mom turned quickly away from the women to hide his own tears. After rubbing his eyes on his sleeves he turned back towards them.

"Can we go to the beach now, or what?"

Four days after they returned from vacation, Patrick was back in the hospital. His skin was a dark tan and he could still smell the salt water in his own hair. He had known it was coming. This one would last more than a week, maybe even a month, he figured. But it was worth it. His vacation had been his freedom and he didn't care that now his breathing test numbers had decreased to dangerously low levels. He felt ok- a little bit of chest pain from the mucus and coughing, but he wasn't terribly symptomatic.

He reached to his bedside table and pulled out his laptop computer. Seth had brought Patrick ten new movies, all burned onto DVDs so he could play it on his computer. Patrick was thrilled that he now had ten more movies not only to watch, but also to add to his archive. He kept a detailed list of all the movies he owned, alphabetized and by genre. Horror was his favorite and was by far the longest list in his archive. He opened the file from his computer and as he finished entering the last of the new titles, Terry popped in for her after work visit.

"Hiya, kid," she greeted him and plopped herself down on a chair by Patrick's bedside.

Patrick took a look at his mother. She looked exhausted. Her blonde hair was pulled back in a messy ponytail and her eyes were heavy from fatigue. She had been working late nights in order to complete her college coursework during the mornings. He loved having her visit, and she never missed a day, but he always felt a twinge of guilt when he saw how exhausted she was by the time she arrived. The drive wasn't on her way home from work and she often had to rush from work to the hospital and then home to take care of his brother and sister. He knew it was a lot for her, and he felt particularly bad because this hospitalization was in a way, his own fault.

"Hey, ma" he answered. "You look beat."

"Yeah. It's been a long day. Did Dr. Hammond come by?"

"Uh, huh," he nodded, "More of the same. IV antibiotics and more nebulizers. Its *pseudomonas* again."

Patrick could see Terry's relief when he told her that the bacteria in his lungs were *Psuedomonas* again and not *Cepacia*. It was unspoken between the two of them, but they both feared that at any time Dr. Hammond might come in and reveal that Patrick's sputum sample was growing *Cepacia*. The incurable.

"Ok. Well, hopefully it won't be too long this time," she answered, trying to be nonchalant but not doing a good job of hiding her relief from Patrick.

They sat silent for a few minutes. The silence was uncomfortable as Patrick wondered if now would be a good time to ask.

"Mom?" Patrick said quietly.

"Yes?" Terry said.

"I've been thinking a lot about my future. Its just a matter of time before I get really bad, and well, I was thinking I'd like to get married." He was choking out the words and braced himself for Terry's reaction.

"Married?" Terry said with a steady voice. Her head was swelling and she felt dizzy, but kept it hidden from Patrick's innocent eyes.

"Yeah. We both know I'd be really lucky to reach 25, and well, I just don't want to miss out. I really want to propose to Shawna. I want to buy her a ring. I want to know what it feels like to propose and to get married. I saved up my money, but I wanted to make sure you wouldn't be mad first," Patrick said.

Terry thought about it. He had a point. True, they were just kids, but even if Patrick survived to be 18, the legal age for marriage, he might not be healthy enough to get himself down the aisle.

"Are you sure?" she asked.

He nodded.

"Well, if that's what you want to do, then I'm not going to stand in your way. You should talk to Shawna's parents too, though," Terry answered. She felt like screaming as the words came out of her mouth. This wasn't the way it was supposed to be. Her son was supposed to be a healthy sixteen-year-old boy, not worrying about whether or not he would live long enough to get married. He was supposed to be out drinking beer and getting into trouble. He wasn't supposed to be sitting next to her in a hospital bed asking for her permission to propose to his sixteen year old girlfriend.

But life was as it was and Terry couldn't think about what should be. There wasn't enough room in her heart to have that kind of pain. She had to fill her heart with love for Patrick and her other children. And so, the answer, was, of course, yes.

Patrick was 17 when Shawna broke up with him. She had worn his diamond ring for a year, but eventually, the relationship fell apart. They remained good friends, but being in the hospital every day with her fiancé wasn't the way she wanted to spend her teen years. Patrick had missed the prom because he had been in the hospital and eventually, she broke the news to him. Terry was proud of the way Patrick handled it. He wasn't angry or even bitter. Even though he was hurt, he understood. It wasn't exactly a hard concept to grasp. Patrick was in the hospital these days more than he was out and Shawna had an active social life at school. Patrick, on the other hand, was being privately tutored. It just wasn't going to work.

But Patrick was resilient and it wasn't long before he was out and about again with his brother and friends. There were parties every weekend and whenever Patrick could make one, he'd be there. He wasn't holding back on life by any means.

By age 18 Patrick was the neighborhood "beer pong" champion, and although she didn't officially approve of underage drinking, Terry didn't give her son a hard time. She considered it as him reaching out to his Irish heritage, in which he always took great pride. Besides, he was having fun, and that was all that mattered to her. He was responsible and she had to trust that he would make good decisions and he always did. He was extremely close with his brother and cousins and so she trusted that they would all watch out for each other.

She wanted him to be happy outside the hospital, because nowadays, being in the hospital was no longer all fun and games. Since he was now 18, he wasn't eligible for admission to the children's hospital. He was now an adult and therefore was admitted as such. Gone were the video games and ice cream. Gone were the colorful walls and pediatric nurses. Patrick's hospitalizations were a lot more dismal for him and he became more and more depressed each day the doctors told him he couldn't go home.

It was at the adult hospital that I met Patrick. I hadn't had a chance to read his entire chart, but my sign-out told me his basic story and that the plan was to discharge him home tomorrow.

I remember vividly walking to Patrick's room. I was excited to meet him. He was only 18 years old and was the very first cystic fibrosis patient that I would have on my service. I was a second year resident and I knew I wanted to go into pulmonary medicine and critical care, so it was about time I learn about taking care of a patient with cystic fibrosis. It was also a nice change of pace from the chest pain patients and the confused elderly patients with pneumonias. I was in my twenties and so Patrick was closer to my age than any of my other patients and the idea of taking care of someone so young was exciting to me. As I walked to the room, I thought about what kind of conversation I would try to whip up to build a rapport with my new, young patient.

His room was furthest from the nurses' station since Patrick was so young, able to walk on his own and take care of himself. So, it made sense that the nurses assigned him the room furthest from eyesight. When I finally reached his room, I wasn't surprised to find an isolation cart outside his doorway. Infections were the nemesis of cystic fibrosis. The red sign on his door shouted at me as I gowned up: "CONTACT ISOLATION! Gloves and gowns are required at all times". I dressed in the familiar yellow garb and knocked on the door.

"Yeah?" I heard from inside.

I opened the door and went in to greet my patient. The room was dark and his bed was on the far side of the room. The isolation hit me like a brick. The shades were drawn despite the fact that it was early afternoon. Patrick had his computer on his lap and I understood why the room was so dark; he was watching a movie. Screams and blaring music emanated from the computer speakers. I waited for him to turn it down so that I could say hello, but he didn't move.

"Hi, Mr. O'Connor," I said. As soon as I said the words I felt silly. I always called my patient "Mr." as the majority of them were vastly older than I was. But Patrick was a teenager. I felt embarrassed after my words were out.

"Uh, I'm Dr. Van Scoy," I stuttered. I was expecting him to pause his movie or at least look up at me, but he did no such thing. His gaze never left his computer screen.

"How are you doing?" I asked, feeling uncomfortable and annoyed that he wasn't paying any attention to me at all.

"The same," he said flatly.

"Are you having any shortness of breath?" I asked. I felt stupid, and my hopes of striking up a conversation were fading quickly. I suddenly wanted nothing more than to get out of the room.

"Uh, ok, good," I answered as Patrick shook his head 'no' to my question. "Any pain?"

The same head nod.

'Ok...what now?' I thought to myself

"Uh, can I listen to your lungs?" I asked sheepishly.

He leaned forward, exposing his back but without a word. 'Why did he *hate* me so much?' I wondered.

He was wearing a green T-shirt and a pair of sweatpants. Normally, I would place my stethoscope underneath the shirt to get the best listen to the lungs that I could, but in my discomfort, I just placed the bell of my stethoscope on his back.

"Deep breath," I instructed.

He obliged, movie blaring, never looking away from the screen.

I listened to the crackles of mucus as he inhaled and exhaled and looked around his room. On the window sill there was a remote controlled helicopter and a pile of DVDs. Clothing was strewn about amidst car magazines and a portable video game player. My eyes were curious as they combed the room; none of my other patients' rooms had so much *stuff.*

Patrick leaned back, ending my pulmonary exam for me.

"Uh, alright. I guess I'll come back later," I said.

"Am I going home tomorrow?" Patrick asked suddenly, his eyes leaving the screen for the very first time.

"That's what I hear. I need to just confirm with Dr. Hammond and I'll get your paperwork started," I answered, taken aback by his eyes suddenly meeting mine.

"Ok," he said, and turned back to the movie.

I headed for the door, ripped off my isolation gown and closed the door behind me to sounds of a screeching damsel in distress.

I stood still outside his room for a moment to reflect on what had just happened. I hadn't interviewed him. I hadn't even really examined him. *What would I say on rounds?* Should I go back in and demand that he allow me to do my job? Could I face Dr. Hammond, my attending, whom I wanted to impress with my stellar clinical skills? How could I present this patient to him? I had essentially no information about the state of his symptoms or even a decent physical exam!

Maybe I'll stop back before rounds and see if his movie is over, I decided. In the meantime, I made my way to his chart. When I found it, I had to grasp it with two hands. It was entirely too thick to lift with just one. I flipped it open and papers spilled out from inside the binder. I looked at the admission date on one of the papers that came loose; Patrick had been in the hospital for five weeks. *Five weeks.* I turned to the beginning and began to read the pages.

Patrick had been non-compliant with his medications for a week before his admission while he had been on vacation and his breathing test results had been terrible when he had first been admitted. I had never seen numbers so low. He had grown huge quantities of bacteria in his sputum and had been on five different antibiotics during his admission. He had required a lot of IV pain medication to control the chest pains he experienced when his rib cage moved with every breath. As I read through the pages I saw his daily breathing tests- five weeks worth. I saw his daily blood draws-five weeks worth. His vitals had been taken every six to eight hours for five weeks. There were many days the nurses documented "patient refused" in the area where his blood pressure and temperature should have been.

As I read I began to understand the boy in the dark room I had just left. He had a resident check in on him every day, ask him the same questions over and over, do the same physical exam and tell him the same thing: "we'll send you home as soon as your numbers improve." I was just another resident to him, with the same questions and the same answers. The encounter I had just had with him suddenly made sense. I looked at the breathing test result from today. It was 50%, which was still very low, but acceptable to send him home. I immediately began the discharge paperwork, knowing that after rounds, Dr. Hammond would give me the green light to send Patrick home.

He was my first cystic fibrosis patient and all I did was his discharge paperwork, but in that brief patient encounter, I gained an understanding into living with cystic fibrosis that I couldn't have learned otherwise.

It only took three weeks or so after Patrick's discharge for him to find himself back in Dr. Hammond's office. Terry had called the office the week before because Patrick had spiked a fever, and Dr. Hammond had asked her to make an appointment one week after dropping off a sputum sample. Terry and Patrick found themselves once again in the all-too-familiar environment of Dr. Hammond's office.

The breathing test sat on the table, awaiting the doctor's review. Patrick saw that the number was 20% and he knew that it meant he was to go back in the hospital. A group of guys were going camping that weekend and he would have to miss it, yet again.

When Dr. Hammond came in, Patrick knew immediately by the look on his face.

"I have *Cepacia*, don't I?" he said before Dr. Hammond could even sit on his stool.

"Yes, you do," he answered simply. His eyes were now on the breathing test and he took a deep breath before going into yet another speech about needing to hospitalize Patrick.

"I'm not going in," Patrick said. "I'm done. I want to be done. I want to go on hospice."

Terry felt the pit of her stomach rise into her throat like a lump of coal and she swallowed hard to alleviate the pain. The word was like a Mack truck hitting her square between the eyes. Hospice. Where old people went to die. And now, her little boy was saying the word right now, right in front of her.

Dr. Hammond showed no signs of surprise. "Well, that's an option we can certainly discuss," he said, cautiously, looking over at Terry to try and read how she was feeling. Terry stared blankly, but nodded her head for him to continue.

"Hospice can be a wonderful thing and if its right for you, then we'll help get you set up. But first I want to make sure you understand exactly what it means," Dr. Hammond said.

Patrick sat attentively and listened as the doctor explained the process. He listened as he explained that a patient can enter hospice when they have a terminal disease and do not have a life expectancy of more than six months. He listened as the doctor told him that he would be forgoing any attempts at curative treatments for his cystic fibrosis and for his bacterial infections, but instead his treatment would focus more on pain and symptom relief. He listened as Dr. Hammond explained the different levels of hospice: home hospice, nursing home hospice and inpatient hospice. The hospice company could deliver everything he needed directly to his home and help train his mother how to administer prescribed medications based on his symptoms and pain levels. They would send a nurse out daily for him and they would even deliver a hospital bed to his house if they wanted or needed it. Or, he could choose to go to an inpatient unit.

It sounded like heaven to Patrick. He would only need to take medications to keep him comfortable and wouldn't have to go through all the different treatments, unless he absolutely needed them and chose to take them. He listened through the whole speech and afterwards asked Dr. Hammond "So, exactly how many nebulizers will I *have* to take?"

Dr. Hammond answered as best as he knew how, knowing that Patrick's real question was "just how *normal* can I be?"

After leaving the doctor's office, Terry never questioned Patrick's decision. After all, he was eighteen years old, almost nineteen, and was wise beyond his years. Although at times she had to fight against the overwhelming urge to beg him to continue his treatments, to beg him to try and save himself, to fight longer, but she knew how resolute her son could be and she knew that above all, spending his remaining time in the hospital was not a option Patrick would entertain. Dr. Hammond felt it was a reasonable decision and Terry felt reassured by private discussions with him. He reassured her that she wasn't a terrible mother for allowing Patrick to forego aggressive treatment. And so, it didn't take long for Terry to be at peace with Patrick's decision and they discussed it often and in depth. She was certain he was making the right choice for himself and, as always, offered her unwavering support.

After one of their many conversations on the living room sofa, Patrick turned to Terry with a sparkle in his eye.

"Let's have a party!" he said.

"A party?" she asked, taken off guard.

"Yeah. A celebration of life party. I want to do something really fun. We can rent out the Irish Pub and invite everyone and just have a party," he said, getting more excited as he spoke. "Whaddya think?"

"Sure, Patrick. I think that's a great idea. We Irish can get through anything with a party and a little beer!" she laughed. "Let's do it!"

The hall was booked for three weekends from then and Patrick invited all his friends and family. The preparations were like a whirlwind; although Patrick was relatively well right now, he *was* officially on home hospice and they both knew that the *cepacia* living in his lungs could rear its ugly head at any time. Even though Patrick was declining dramatically on paper, his spirit was doing no such thing. Perhaps he couldn't run about and certainly had periods of chest pain and shortness of breath, but in the weeks leading up to his Celebration of Life Party, he lived pretty normally. The family spent a lot of time together and Patrick spent almost every night playing cards with his brother, sister and cousins. Everyone wanted to be near Patrick and he loved every minute of it.

On the day of the party, the hall was decked out in explosions of green and white. Shamrocks lined the walls and Irish music was piped in from the speakers above. Patrick's cousins surprised him by with an enormous banner that read "Celebration of Life" in enormous green, white and silver lettering. In the spaces between the letters each family member and friend scrawled messages to Patrick. It hung boldly on the wall and served as a visual reminder to Patrick of how loved he truly was. As the guests arrived Terry watched as they stood awkwardly, not sure how to act or what to say. Was this a death party? Should they express their condolences to Patrick and his family? What should they say to Patrick? But the instant Patrick greeted them, all those thoughts soon melted away.

During the party, Terry watched lovingly as Patrick laughed and joked with his friends. He played host and greeted each guest as they came to his bash, pointing them in the direction of the food and drink. He was truly the 'belle of the ball' and Terry and Gary couldn't help but feel the pride and love flow through them like a river. The party raged for hours and by the end of the evening any uneasy feelings of awkwardness dissipated into food, fun and laughter. By two in the morning, when Terry could no longer beat back her fatigue, she watched from a table as Patrick escorted the last guest to the door. Terry chuckled to herself as she realized the irony that Patrick was, in fact, the last one standing.

Even though the doctors had prepared them for a rapid and steady decline, Patrick remained stable for the next several months. He took it easy at home, resting often and had variable periods of pain and shortness of breath, but it took the doctors by surprise at just how long Patrick remained relatively healthy. Terry only called upon the hospice agency every few days in the beginning, and they'd respond promptly by helping with Patrick's painkiller dosages. But eventually, even the largest dose of painkiller was unable to control Patrick's unrelenting chest pain. His cough was worsening, which only made the pain worse and he wasn't able to generate enough force to cough out the mucus in his airways.

It soon became clear that Patrick would require IV pain medications and the hospice nurse questioned Patrick about how he wanted to move forward. Patrick and Terry both agreed that in order for Patrick to have rest and calm, home wasn't the place to be anymore. They had two large dogs running around and the house was always bustling with activity. Besides, Patrick didn't want to interrupt Seth and Kara's busy lives with hospital beds and IV poles. He was adamant that he wanted life to go on and that he wanted no part of disrupting the natural flow of life.

Terry was astounded at the ease with which Patrick took to the inpatient hospice facility. When he arrived, he showed no signs of fear, or even of hesitancy. His movements were slow from the pain medications, but he refused to ask Terry or Gary for any assistance getting inside. They were greeted by a petite brunette woman named Karen as they entered the registration room off the main lobby.

"Hello!" she greeted. "You must be Patrick. Dr. Hammond called and told me to expect you. I have your paperwork all ready and we just need you to sign a few documents so we can get you up to your room. I know you had a long trip."

She motioned them into a sitting room that looked like it was straight out of a Martha Stewart magazine. A packet of papers laid on a coffee table. Patrick took a seat on the sofa and Terry realized as she watched him collapse into the cushions just how much energy he was expending just to stand and walk.

Karen could also sense Patrick's fatigue and so she dove right into her speech. "Once you get settled in your room, we can go over this in more detail," she said, handing Patrick a glossy brochure about the facility. "If you're feeling up to it, I can give you a tour of all the amenities we have here. This pamphlet goes into our history, but you can glance through that at your leisure if you're interested. For now, let's just get you registered. Here is some information about the amenities and services we provide. We try to make this place feel like a second home, not only for you, but also for your family. We have a kitchen, a TV room and a small library that you and your family are free to use. Again, you can flip through that upstairs."

"Your home nurse sent me over all your home hospice information, so I have copies of all your medical information and insurance information, so really the only paperwork we need you to fill out today is our waiver of life sustaining measures," she was gentle as she said the words and Terry could see that Karen was proceeding cautiously, so-as not to rush Patrick or overwhelm him as she handed him the documents.

"This basically says that upon coming here, you understand that should your heart stop, or if you were to stop breathing, that you would not receive CPR or a breathing machine as part of your hospice program. We don't provide any life sustaining measures, but instead offer you medications and treatments as much as required to keep you comfortable and as pain free as possible," she explained.

Patrick was nodding as she spoke. He had already had this discussion both with Dr. Hammond and with the home hospice nurse, but the inpatient hospice had its own paperwork to file, just to make sure everyone was on the same page. They were.

After the registration process was over, Karen led them through the facility and up to the main wing where Patrick would be staying. The inside of the building was warm and airy, with gardens and windows scattered about. It was clear that they made an effort to make the facility as aesthetically pleasing as possible, despite the reality that this was where people went to die.

As they approached the patient areas, the interior resembled a hospital unit with the nurses, monitors and nursing stations. There were the usual supplies, IV bags and medications, but the profound difference was the lack of noise. It was quiet. Ghostly quiet. As they walked Terry could hear Patrick's breathing louder than anything else. As they passed the patient rooms, Terry couldn't help but peer inside and feel uncomfortable. All the other patients seemed two hundred years older than Patrick, with heads covered in gray hair and wrinkled skin stained by decades of life.

Terry shuddered as she looked at Patrick and tried to imagine him lying among these old people. Perhaps they had made the wrong decision. Patrick didn't belong here. He was walking, talking. He was the antithesis of what lay in the beds here. He was youth. But, he was also dying, and Terry had to remind herself of that as they finally reached Patrick's room.

They were greeted by a nurse, Stan, who offered Patrick a hospital gown, which he quickly refused.

"No, thanks," Patrick said. "I have my own clothes."

Terry chuckled and smiled at Stan. "Patrick's never worn a hospital gown in his entire life. He's more of a T-shirt and sweatpants kind of kid."

Stan raised his eyebrows. "Well, then!" he joked and tossed the gown dramatically across the room. "How about *that?*"

Patrick laughed as his eyes studied his room. It wasn't much different than a hospital room. He was a little disappointed because the last thing he wanted to do was be in the hospital, but at least the rest of the place was nice.

For the next few days, Patrick had a constant flow of visitors. In between his shots of morphine, he had friends, cousin, aunts, uncles, and grandparents—all coming to visit him in the hospice facility. It got to be so overwhelming that Terry had to limit visitors to immediate family. She wanted Patrick to get to rest and for the first few days, he spent his entire day with visitors streaming in and out. As the days passed, the hospice nurses increased his pain medications. He was comfortable and although groggy he still was able to enjoy card games and movies. During the daytime, Patrick would walk the halls and raid the kitchen for ice cream. Having a patient moving about was quite different for the nurses. Most of their patients were confused, elderly people who hadn't walked in years. But Patrick was a burst of motion, almost a blur as he strolled the hallways of an otherwise motionless ward. By the evening, his energy would dissipate and he'd spend most of his time on the sofa in the TV room playing games or watching movies which his brother, sister or cousins.

Terry stayed in Patrick's room every night. The nurses had rolled in an extra bed for her to spend the nights, while Gary took the kids home to get ready for school the next day. The dark nights were peaceful for the two of them, and Terry and Patrick could spend hours talking if Patrick had the energy. There were many times that Patrick was still lucent through the drugs and it allowed for precious conversation that Terry cherished. At the end of tonight's conversation, Patrick had asked his mom to help him take a shower, a request that had startled Terry. He wasn't one to ask for help, but Terry was always there to provide him with it, should he need it.

Patrick's life was coming to an end, and Terry knew it as she held him there, patting him dry after his shower. The spewing of mucus was over, but there was undoubtedly more to come. He was weaker tonight than she had ever seen him, but the peace he had reached in the last week at the hospice facility and with his family steadied her fear.

She helped him into his pajamas, and he fell asleep as soon as his head hit the pillow but Terry lay awake listening to his labored breathing. A few hours went by and Patrick stirred, woke up and in a state of brief confusion, tried to get out of bed.

"What do you need, Patrick?" Terry asked, sitting up from her cot.

"I want some ice cream," he answered, so groggy that his voice seemed unfamiliar.

"Ok, I'll go get you some, but you stay in bed, ok? I'll bring it to you," Terry said. She glanced at the clock and it was three AM. Patrick often craved ice cream in the middle of the night; it was a habit he had picked up from all the years of being at the children's hospital.

When Terry returned from the kitchen with Patrick's treat, she sat on the edge of his bed and gently shook him to wake him. He didn't move. She immediately put her head on his chest to see if he was breathing, and he was. She could hear the crackles of mucus deep inside his lungs. She shook him more vigorously, calling to him, but there was no response.

She jetted to the nurses station and found Lisa, his evening nurse reading a magazine.

"Patrick isn't waking up!" Terry said, trying to keep her voice from sounding frantic. The signed paperwork burned in the back of her mind. She had to stay even keeled, she couldn't panic. She had to accept that Patrick might not wake up, and that Lisa was not able to do anything to reverse it. It was Patrick's wish. It was Patrick's wish. She repeated the words over and over silently in her mind.

Lisa stood up smoothly and headed towards the room. Her calm demeanor was a stark contrast to the panic in Terry's mind, so she tried to latch on to Lisa's state of mind as Terry followed her back to the room.

Lisa called out to Patrick but he did not respond. Her voice was quiet and gentle and her movements were slow and steady. She pulled the oxygen monitor down from the rack that hung over Patrick's bed and placed it on his finger. While she waited for the pulse oximeter to register the reading, she placed her stethoscope on his chest and listened. One of the other nurses was now hanging by the door as she had heard the calls to Patrick.

The oxygen monitor showed a reading of 70%. Even Terry knew that was low. It was happening.

"Call the on-call doctor," Lisa directed to the nurse standing at the doorway.

"He's in a coma, isn't he?" Terry asked.

"I can't say for sure yet, but his oxygen is pretty low," as Lisa spoke she reached for a thermometer.

Terry clutched her hands together. As Lisa measured his temperature, Terry's eyes stayed fixated on Patrick, hoping he would open his eyes and speak to her. But there was nothing.

"We can put some oxygen on him and see if it helps, if you like. But I know that Patrick hated having to wear the mask."

"Yeah. No oxygen. He hated it. He absolutely hated it," Terry replied. Saying the words was difficult.

"He's on his way in," the other nurse called from the hallway, referring to the hospice on-call physician.

"103.1." Lisa said as the thermometer beeped in her hand. She looked up at Terry, observing her desperate eyes as they searched for any signs of awareness in Patrick.

Terry nodded and reached for her cell phone to make the calls. Patrick was slipping away.

The house doctor, Dr. Tanner, arrived about thirty minutes later. Patrick still hadn't opened his eyes or stirred. He remained still and peaceful, still wearing his favorite Guinness sweatpants with the shamrock on the thigh. The only noise was a soft gurgling coming from inside his chest.

"Hello, Mrs. O'Connor," he said as he reached out his hand to offer to Terry.

"Hi," she said quietly.

"The nursing team has filled me in on everything that's happened and it seems that the oxygen levels have dropped to a point where his brain can no longer function, which is why he isn't responding to us," he began to explain as he reviewed the monitors and looked Patrick over.

"Is he in a coma?" Terry asked.

"Well, that's a hard term to define, but I'd say he is non-responsive," Dr. Tanner said.

"But what does that mean? Is he ever going to speak to me again?" Terry said, surprised at how hostile her words sounded as they came out.

"I wish I could say for sure," Dr. Tanner answered, "but right now I think it could go either way."

It was a non-answer. Patrick had always hated when doctors gave 'non-answers'. And this was the ultimate one. Just as Terry was ready to ask her next question, Gary, Seth and Kara came rushing into the room. Their eyes were red and the three of them looked disheveled. As they rushed to his side, the family wept at Patrick's bedside, but after ten minutes or so, the tears subsided and they were left with just them and Patrick, still and restful.

"This was his choice," Gary reassured Terry. "This was the way he wanted it. We shouldn't be making a fuss over him. That's not what he wanted. Let's try and keep ourselves together." He looked over to Kara and Seth and they nodded in agreement.

Within a few minutes, the family was sitting around Patrick's bedside and on the side of his bed, having normal conversation and talking about Patrick's antics. It wasn't long before the conversation was jovial and they were laughing and joking. Although the nurses had been coming in and out to check on Patrick and his family, it wasn't until a few hours before Lisa approached Terry with a serious look on her face.

This is bad, whatever it is, Terry thought. For a panic stricken moment her eyes darted to Patrick. Had he died while they were chatting? Was that what Lisa was about to tell her? She heaved a sigh of relief when she saw his chest wall moving rhythmically up and down. Terry turned her head back to Lisa and waited for her to begin.

"Um, Mrs. O'Connor," Lisa began. "I'm going to have to put Patrick into a hospital gown. You see, he's going to need a urinary catheter and it's going to be much easier for us to wash and clean him if he isn't in his clothing..." Her voice trailed off.

Terry was confused. That was it?

"I know how much Patrick didn't like hospital gowns, but," Lisa started to say but Terry cut her off.

"It's ok, Lisa," Terry smiled. "He'll understand. He won't like the catheter, but I know he needs it. He can't urinate on his own, right?"

"Exactly. His bladder will get distended and that would be pretty uncomfortable for him," Lisa said.

"Alright, but can you do it in after the kids leave?" Terry asked.

"Sure," Lisa said. "That's not a problem at all."

Terry watched as Lisa left the room. She was touched by how serious Lisa took the necessity of the hospital gown. Lisa was completely in touch with what Patrick would have wanted, and it was clear that Lisa didn't want to do anything at all that would have made Patrick feel pain or be uncomfortable. It was just a piece of cloth, but Lisa took it seriously. Terry knew they had come to the right place. Even the staff understood Patrick. She turned to him and saw him lying there and felt his peace emanating throughout the room.

Patrick had been in a coma for 14 hours when Seth, Kara and Gary began to pack up their things to return home. Only Terry had been staying nights. Patrick hadn't wanted anyone else to stay. He wanted life to go on and for Seth and Kara to continue to 'do their thing' as Patrick would say. Terry walked them down to the main exit and hugged them all goodnight. Gary held her more tightly than usual as they said goodbye and she smiled and waved as they headed to the car.

When she returned back upstairs, she was shocked at what she saw lying in the bed. Lisa had put Patrick in the hospital gown, and laid his clothing neatly on the bed stand next to him. He looked sick. He was shockingly frail and delicate. His skin was white and his hair looked dark next to his face. He looked like a vampire straight out of his own video archive. It was the first time that Patrick looked like someone who was about to die. Terry gathered her composure, checked her fear at the door and climbed into bed next to Patrick. His skin was burning up and sweat was pouring off his body. You could feel the heat from a foot away. His body was in crisis.

Throughout the night, Terry spoke softly in Patrick's ear.

"It's alright. You can go. I'll be alright. Things won't fall apart. *I* won't fall apart. I'll take care of everyone. You don't have to worry. We are all going to be just fine."

Patrick died early the next morning. Even though the doctor had warned Terry that Patrick might linger for several days between life and death, Patrick died quickly. When he died, Terry was by his side, holding his burning hand. Exactly when his breathing slowed to a halt and his heart stopped beating was hard to say. It was hard to define the moment of death. Terry didn't know when the last heartbeat ended. It was smooth and quiet; there were no monitors beeping or frantic cries. It was not an event, but a transition, Patrick's final transition, and it was perfect in every way.

When I met Terry, it was approximately two years after Patrick's death. She had granted me the interview for which I could write the amazing story of Patrick's life and death. As I drove to her workplace (she is now a social worker), I was filled with anxiety about how my interview would go. How on earth could I ask a mother to tell me the intimate details of her son's death? Would I be able to get the words out to ask my questions? Would she be crying hysterically during my interview? What would I say to her and how would I console her? What kind of a burden would my interview place upon her? I was filled with uncertainty when I arrived and had to steady my own knees as I shook her hand in greeting.

Terry immediately made me feel comfortable. She relayed the story of her son's battle with cystic fibrosis with what seemed to me to be incredible ease. I didn't have to ask a lot of questions, she was happy to share and I was shocked at how different her demeanor was to the hysterical grieving mother that I expected.

After Patrick's death, Terry had been surprised by her own reaction. In the weeks and months after he was buried she wondered why it wasn't harder for her. "What's wrong with me?" she wondered. "Why am I not grieving more for the loss of my son? Why am I not hugging his pillow at night and smelling his old clothes like the other mothers who have lost their children? How is it that I am genuinely 'ok'?"

As she told me about those deeply personal questions, I sat forward in my chair, eagerly awaiting her answers. It was a one-word answer: closure.

Terry went on to tell me about how the process of Patrick's hospice stay enabled her and her family to accept and embrace his impending death. She was able to ask him questions: are you scared? What does it feel like? She was able to talk to him and to tell him all the things a mother needs to tell a son. They were able to talk about life and death and to be prepared for what lies ahead. Patrick gave her strength by telling her the way he saw his life.

"I might not have been here long, but I lived life as if I'm 100 years old," he had told her the night before he died.

Hospice provided Terry with acceptance before the death actually happened. It allowed them time to process that he was going to die. It enabled her and her family to let go. They had weeks of closure, weeks of time to learn to accept the inevitable. Terry told me that all that needed to be said had been said and it was that final closure that got her through the impossible. It was the very reason she sat before me answering my probing questions candidly and without hesitation. It was why she maintained her full composure while detailing the way in which her son met death and how she went on afterwards. To Terry, it was hospice that provided her and her family with the closure they needed to survive.

"People can survive things they can't even imagine," Terry says. "You have no idea what you can endure and stride through until you actually go through it. You see so many movies [about death], but it was nothing like that, it was better than that."

Patrick donated his lungs to cystic fibrosis research. He donated all his other organs as well. "Let them take it all!" he had told his mom. Patrick made his contribution to science and my hope is that his story might make its contribution to the education of those parents and patients facing critical and chronic disease.

Chapter Four: Walter's Story

B Y THE TIME I met Walter Atkins, he was already dead. His body lay in the emergency room trauma bay where they had first wheeled him in from the ambulance as my pager went off, my first alert to his presence. The ER doctors had acted fast, but the CT scan of his head came back showing a devastating bleed within his brain. The fact that he was only 29 years old, exactly one year younger than me, was the part of the story that resonated in my head as Arvin, the neurology resident told me the results of the CT scan over the phone.

"There is a midline shift," he told me, "with some tonsillar herniation. The family is at the bedside..." His voice trailed away and his hesitancy to complete his sentence was apparent. Arvin was a new resident and this wasn't going to be an easy family discussion.

"I'll be right there," I reassured him and hung up the phone. It was late and I had been taking my final walk through the unit before heading home for the evening. With my residency years behind me, I was now the ICU fellow on home call tonight, but I had decided to linger around in the unit anyway, just in case. Good decision, I thought to myself. Arvin was a brilliant resident, but he would be the first to admit that communication wasn't his strongest asset. His thick Indian accent made him difficult to understand and English was his second language. Although he had perfect comprehension of language, he had a very difficult time translating his thoughts into words. In this situation, all the medical knowledge in the world wouldn't make one shred of difference. It was all about finding the right words. If the CT findings were as severe as Arvin had described, then there was not much we could do to save him...if he wasn't already gone.

As I rode the elevator down from the unit to the emergency room I realized I hadn't asked Arvin the patient's name or even his room number. But the ER was easy enough to navigate and surely Arvin would find me. The elevator door dinged and opened, dumping me in front of the ER's electronic doors. I reached for my ID and slid it through the card slot. Red light. I turned it around and repeated the process. Another red light. The cards never worked right and I could never figure out which orientation was the correct one. After four attempts and four red lights, I was grateful when the doors swung open, activated from the inside. I looked up from the card slot and saw Arvin waving me in. Two problems solved. So far, things were going swimmingly.

"Thanks," I greeted Arvin as I stepped into the emergency room wing, "seven years working in this hospital and I still can't figure out the card swipe." Arvin chuckled as he led me towards the x-ray viewer. Dr. Baxter, one of the ER physicians was seated in front of the machine as we approached, intently looking over a film of someone's shoulder joint. Upon seeing me he jolted aside so that I could use the viewer.

"I guess you're here for the brain bleed, huh?" he said with a blend of relief and eagerness in his voice. The ER in general was very eager to have the ICU patients moved out of the ER and up to the unit as soon as humanly possibly.

"Uh, huh," I responded. "What's his story? Arvin told me about the scan, it sounds bad."

"Yeah, young kid," Dr. Baxter said shaking his head solemnly. "Its terrible, he probably ruptured an aneurysm, parents found him down in his apartment, the scan shows that he's herniating." He pulled up the images on the viewer.

Herniating. There was that word again, the black cloud of neurology. The worst-case scenario. The kiss of death. The precursor to brain death. The word set my mind turning with the cascade of events that would need to happen within the next 24 hours. First, I'd have to perform a neurological exam, which was about as nontechnical a medical test as it comes. The amount of critical information a doctor can get from a simple neurologic exam, armed only with a rubber hammer, a flashlight and a sharp stick is impressive. Compared to CT scans and MRIs, the neurologic exam is dirt cheap- almost free, in fact, but it provides us with more information than the most expensive tests put together. But if the neurologic exam showed that certain brainstem reflexes were absent, well, then that was it. All the expensive testing and surgery and machinery couldn't change the simple fact that the patient was dead.

After my exam, would come the calls to the neurosurgeons, if the ER hadn't called them already, just in case my exam was wrong and there was a possibility for emergency brain surgery. But most of the time, patients with significant herniation are too far gone for surgery anyway.

Then would come the tough part. Explaining. This was the part that Arvin needed me for. He could perform the neurologic exam just as well as I could. He could read the CT scans and make the phone calls. But the explanation was the part that left most young residents, including myself at times, stumbling over their own tongues.

I shook myself out of the future and back into the present as Dr. Baxter navigated the CT images screen for me to view. The grey brain images appeared aligned next to each other, with each subsequent image showing more and more 'white stuff.' The three of us stood silent and still while staring at the pictures.

"Is that blood?" a voice shot out from behind me. Startled, I turned my head and saw that a medical student had snuck up behind me. He was wearing scrubs under his short white coat, so I assumed he was a student rotating in the ER.

"Hi Chris," Dr. Baxter said. "Yeah, unfortunately, it is. All the white you see here is blood in his brain. You can see how the blood is actually pushing the brain tissue over to the side, pressing the brain up against the side of his skull."

Chris made a face. "Not good," he muttered.

"Actually, Chris, since you just got here, this is a good case for you to follow. Dr. Van Scoy, do you mind if Chris hangs out with you while you for awhile?"

I didn't.

"No problem," I told him. "Call me LJ," I said as I held out my hand to shake Chris's hand, "and this is Arvin, my neurology resident."

"Great, thanks," Dr. Baxter said. "LJ is the ICU fellow so you can hang out with her until the patient goes up to the unit. We don't have much else going on down here right now, so this should be more educational for you."

I took one last look at the pictures of my new patient's brain and pressed my lips together. It was time to get started.

"OK, Arvin, why don't you present the case to us and then we'll all go see him together. We've seen his imaging, but let's hear the story," I said, moving towards the chart rack.

Arvin snapped into action with a quick movement, a direct contrast from the stillness he exuded while looking at the image. He straightened himself up so much that he seemed to grow 2 inches taller. He began.

"The patient is a 29 year old white male with no past medical history who was found on the ground in his apartment by his mother earlier this afternoon. She had come over to his apartment after she heard that he hadn't come to work and he didn't return his calls." He paused, his formality fading. "Uh, that's really it. He had no past medical history, so..."

"He's never had any surgery?" I inquired.

"No, never," Arvin answered.

"Medications?" I asked.

Arvin shook his head.

"Recent illnesses?" I prompted.

"Nope."

"Totally healthy?" I was quite surprised. It was unusual that we had a patient with no past medical history at all, but then again, this guy was only 29 years old.

"Yeah, I asked both his parents, no medical problems," Arvin confirmed.

"So, what was his exam like?" I asked. I was going through the formalities since I was going to examine the patient myself, but I also wanted to test Arvin to know how thorough and accurate he had been in assessing the patient before he had called me.

"Well, he is on the ventilator and isn't taking any spontaneous breaths. His pupils are nonreactive, and he doesn't withdraw to any painful stimuli. No gag reflex. No deep tendon reflexes. No oculocephalics. Nothing," Arvin said.

"So, from what you're telling me, he's dead," I prompted.

"Yeah, I believe he is," Arvin answered.

"What about the rest of his exam...heart, lungs," I asked.

Chris looked at me as if I had six heads. He was perplexed and I knew why, but I wanted to give him the opportunity to hear the answer before I explained my question.

"Heart and lungs were normal. Normal heart sounds. Regular heart rate. No murmurs. No arrhythmias. Lungs were clear on both sides," Arvin began rattling off findings and I watched as Chris furrowed his brow in confusion.

"What's the matter, Chris?" I asked, interrupting Arvin as he was telling me about the abdominal exam.

"Well, didn't we just say he is dead? But, uh, now we're saying the heart exam was normal," Chris asked.

"He's brain dead, it's different," Arvin said.

"Well, actually, no," I interrupted, "dead is dead. But what you mean is he did not have a cardiac death. He had a brain death. Well, that's what it seems. We have to go see him to be sure, but if what Arvin is saying is correct, then yes, he is dead even though his heart is beating."

"Oh," Chris said. He opened his mouth to ask another question, but shut it again and looked over at me.

"We'll get there," I reassured him, "let's go see him first and then we'll talk about all the details. If he has herniated, then it's very likely that he is already brain dead. But if not, we'll have to act fast. Was neurosurgery called?"

Dr. Baxter overheard my question and answered from the across the nursing station, "I called Dr. Anteas. He's reviewing the films now."

"What about family?" I asked. "Do they know what's going on?

"I didn't tell them too much, except that it doesn't look good and we are having the neurosurgeons look at his film," Dr. Baxter answered.

"Great," I turned to Arvin, "Lead the way."

Arvin led me into ER Room 2. The room was enclosed by a sliding glass door through which I could see that the curtain was drawn. Underneath the curtain I could see four feet, supposedly the parents, who were sitting on two chairs facing the bed.

"Will you introduce me?" I said to Arvin as I knocked and slid open the glass door. "Its easier for me to break the ice if someone they already know introduces me to them."

"Sure," Arvin said as he pulled open the curtain as we entered the room.

I was taken aback by the couple in front of me, so stoic on their small plastic chairs. Typically when I walk into a room, my eyes first dart to the monitors before addressing the patient or family, just to be sure everything was stable. But in this room, the stillness of these two people drew my eyes to them and only them. I didn't even look at the patient; the parents' faces said it all. They were pale, tear-stained and distraught. I knew that the person who needed the most help was not, in fact, the patient, but instead, his parents. They were in shock.

"This is Dr. Van Scoy," Arvin began and gestured to me. "She's the intensive care fellow."

"Hello," I said softly, holding out my hand for the husband and wife. They each meagerly took turns shaking my hand in silence, barely looking up from the floor. "This is Chris, one of our medical students," I said, finalizing the formalities.

Chris silently nodded towards the duo.

"I'm just going to examine your son and then we'll talk about what we're going to do from here, alright?" I said gently before heading over to the stretcher where my patient lay.

As I looked at him I saw a young man, with a ventilator tube jutting from his clean-shaven jaw. His eyes were shut and his skin was flushed with color. Hardly the way anyone would expect a dead man to look. I first placed my hand on his shins, to feel if they had warmth. They did. Blood was perfusing to his legs. Next, I touched his arms and felt the same thing. The heart was pumping blood to his extremities. His heart, after all, was as healthy as a horse. My eyes finally went to the monitors. His heart rate was 80 beats per minute and his blood pressure a perfect 120/80. The ventilator sounds whirred without any alarms and I could hear the air whoosh in and out of his perfectly normal lungs. His body was as healthy as mine was, but his brain was destroyed. As I thought about the tragedy of it all, I realized I hadn't even caught the patient's name, so I reached down to his hand and turned it ever so slightly so that I would expose the name on his armband. Walter. Walter Atkins.

I went through the rest of the exam as quickly and gingerly as possible so as not to make any sudden moves or disturb his body in any way. The room was silent and every move I made felt like a tidal wave amidst the stillness in the air. I tried to keep my attention solely on Walter, even though I could feel the presence of Arvin, Chris and Walter's parents' eyes on me, watching my every move.

I confirmed Arvin's report of the physical exam; it was completely normal-except I hadn't tested the brain function yet. Before I started, I glanced over at

110

the drips on the pole above Walter's head. Only IV fluids were being infused, no medications. Walter's body didn't require any medications, but we were giving him the fluid since he couldn't eat or drink and probably hadn't for quite some time.

"Did he get any meds?" I asked Arvin.

Arvin nodded. "When they intubated him, they gave him some sedative and fentanyl."

"Right," I said, flashing a look at Arvin that I hoped said 'damn it.' The medications would alter the neurologic exam that I was about to perform, making it impossible to make any definitive decisions based on the exam. Sedatives and narcotics affect the neural reflexes in such a way that you can't actually declare someone officially brain dead until those medications completely wore off. That would take approximately 6 hours. And for any family, 6 hours was a long time to wait without knowing if your loved one is dead or alive.

I took out my penlight and gently lifted Walter's eyelids open. "I'm going to shine a light in your eyes, Walter," I said, more for his parents' benefit than for his. I knew he couldn't hear me. The pupils didn't move when exposed to the light, as they should if the reflex was functioning. Next, I took out a swab of cotton from the cabinet next to the stretcher and twirled its end into a fine point. Again, I lifted his eyelid and dabbed the cotton tip onto the surface of his eyeball. There was no reflex for him to blink. He was 0 for 2. Next, I checked his oculocephalic reflex, what we call 'doll's eyes'. I took Walter's head in my hands and moved his head from side to side, watching his eyes. They remained fixed, his gaze not moving as I turned his head. Not good. Next, I looked at the ventilator's set rate. It was set at 16. Walter was breathing at a rate of 16, which told me that the ventilator was doing all the breathing and Walter's brain wasn't triggering any extra breaths. Since the brain tells your lungs to breathe, even when someone is on a breathing machine they might breathe over the vent, which we call "over breathing". Over breathing is a good sign. It means that the brain is stimulating extra breaths, independent of the ventilator. But in Walter's case, there were no extra breaths. I reached over to the tube jutting out of his mouth and jostled it ever so slightly, to see if I could trigger Walter to cough or gag from the stimulation in the back of his throat. Nothing.

A glance over to Arvin and we silently agreed: he was gone. There was still one test I had left to do, which involved squirting cold water into his ear, but I decided to defer that test until later, considering we'd have to repeat the same exam in 6 hours after the medications wore off. Rather, I thought, my time was better spent talking to the neurosurgeons and then initiating what was going to be a rather difficult discussion with Walter's mom and dad.

Dr. Anteas was on the other end of the phone as Dr. Baxter handed it to me from over the counter. No sooner had Arvin, Chris and I walked out of Walter's room then Dr. Anteas had called in to the ER to talk with the ICU team about the case. And I was it.

"Hi Dr. Anteas," I said. "This is LJ."

"Oh, hey LJ. How's it going?" he said cheerily.

"It's going," I answered. My standard reply. "Did you take a look at these films?"

"Yeah, from what I hear, he has no brainstem reflexes," Dr. Anteas said.

"Uh huh. I just saw him and I wasn't able to elicit any reflex, but he did get some ativan and narcotics during his intubation, so I can't say for sure," I answered.

"OK, I already spoke with Dr. Conn and he is willing to take him to the IR suite and take a look to see if there is anything he can coil," he said.

"Really?" I didn't hide the shock in my voice. IR stood for interventional radiology, which meant they were considering just that: an intervention.

"At least its something we can try. Are you considering taking him to surgery? I just assumed that he's too far gone for that."

"He probably is, but there's a possibility we could put in a drain, but we'll have to see what happens in IR," Dr. Anteas said.

"Sounds like a plan," I said, newly hopeful since he thought there was a possibility for an intervention.

"I'm on my way in," Dr. Anteas said. "I'll see you in a few minutes."

"OK, thanks," I responded and returned the phone to Dr. Baxter's outstretched arm.

"They're taking him to IR?" Dr. Baxter asked as returned the phone to the cradle for me.

"Apparently so," I answered. "I'll get him a bed in the unit in the meantime and we'll go from there."

Arvin, I could see, had already turned to the computer to place the orders while I made a few phone calls to procure a bed for Walter in the ICU. Once the calls were made, I turned to Chris, who had a look of confusion spread from ear to ear.

"Confused yet?" I asked him with a smile.

"Completely and totally," he answered.

Once the admission paperwork and calls were completed, I decided I had been stalling long enough. It was past time that I to talk to Walter's family. Arvin was working furtively on his admission orders, so I motioned to Chris to come along with me for "The Discussion". I had a lot of explaining to do for Walter's parents and for Chris, who thankfully wasn't bombarding me with questions just yet. Perhaps he could sense the angst in my demeanor and the subsequent stress I was undoubtedly exuding. The Discussion was near and although I've had many of these conversations with families in the past, it wasn't very common that the patient was an otherwise healthy young man, particularly one who was so close in age to me. How would Walter's parents feel getting this information from me, a young woman only a few years older than their dying son? I had to shake it off and press on and I had procrastinated long enough.

"Let's talk to the parents and then you and I will go over the medical details once we have everything sorted out, ok?" I said to Chris as I once again knocked on the glass sliding door leading to Walter's room to signal my entrance to the room.

Walter's family was exactly as I had left them. I wondered if they had even breathed since I had left the room.

"How are you doing?" I asked them as an icebreaker. I was met with silent shrugs. But it was a start. I looked around for another chair but didn't see any within the immediate area. This was going to be a different experience for me as well; I didn't commonly have discussions like this in the emergency room. Most of the time I preferred to have the patients settled into the unit before making any firm judgment or recommendations. But in this case, I was making an exception. It was going to take a long time for them to process the information I was going to give them and usually it took families many hours, even days, for the reality to sink in. The sooner we started the conversation, the better.

"Well, let me start off by saying that I'm terribly sorry to meet you under these circumstances. In case you forgot, my name is Dr. Van Scoy and I'm one of the critical care fellows. The ER called me so that we can get Walter upstairs to the intensive care unit," I said, the words rolling off my tongue. It was my typical intro that I resorted to when I was otherwise at a loss for words.

Walter's mother reached out her hand. "I'm Ilene and this is my husband Jake," she managed to say as she shook my hand.

Jake looked at the ground but nodded his head in a feeble hello.

"I'm not exactly sure how much Dr. Baxter has already explained to you, so why don't you summarize for me what you've understood so far and we'll pick it up from there," I said. It was as good as a place as any to start, and with any luck, they may tell me that they already knew he was probably brain dead. That would make my job a lot easier.

"Well, we know he had a big bleed in his head and that it doesn't look very good, but other than that, we don't know how this happened or if the surgeons are going to take him to surgery or what," Ilene said, her words picking up speed as she went. "I just don't understand what happened"

"Ok, well, you're exactly right," I began. "Walter did have a major bleed within his brain. There's a lot of blood in his brain right now. Whether it's the result of some sort of fall or trauma or if it was a brain aneurysm that ruptured, we just don't know yet."

As I spoke a terrible thought crept into my head. I didn't know if he had a urine drug screen or an alcohol level when he arrived. This would be much worse if it turned out that the bleed was after a drunken fall or a cocaine binge. I hoped that wasn't the case, for his parent's sake, and made a mental note to myself to remember to make sure the ER had sent off those tests.

Trying not to look or seem distracted, I continued in my monologue.

"The cause of the bleed isn't terribly relevant at this point, although if it was an aneurysm, the interventional radiologist doctors may be able to place a coil inside the aneurysm in order to plug it up and contain the bleeding or prevent another rupture. The problem with that is, there has been a lot of brain damage already, and the coil can't do anything about damage already done, but it's something we're looking in to."

A look of hope crossed Walter's dad's otherwise expressionless face, so much that I began backpedalling immediately.

"Unfortunately, though, there is a chance that Walter's brain is already so badly damaged, that it may not even be functioning any more, which is called brain death," I said it as bluntly as I could, the words sounding vulgar as they resonated in the room. But it had to be said. I paused for some kind of reaction, got none and thus continued, slipping into formalities.

"Earlier, when we were examining Walter, we did some very simple tests that help us to determine whether the brain is actually functioning. Simple things like when I flashed the light in his eyes to see if his pupils would get smaller or when I moved the breathing tube around to see if would gag. And, well, unfortunately, he didn't respond," I said. Again, I paused and was met with blank stares. Keep going, LJ, I told myself. Keep going.

"We have him hooked up to the ventilator, not because his lungs are sick, though, but because his brain isn't telling him to breathe...which is another sign that his brain is not functioning...so he's fully dependent on the life support," I was beginning to stutter. I looked over at Chris for just a moment, just to have someplace else to divert my eyes, but his face was as blank and dismal as Walter's parents'.

"What are you saying, doc, that he has brain damage?" Jake said, his voice cracking.

"Well, yes. He most definitely has brain damage, but I guess what I'm trying to say is that I'm very concerned that his brain is at risk of dying completely, if it hasn't already," I answered. "The most worrisome thing is that his brain is actually herniating."

I paused to see if there was any reaction to the word. There wasn't.

"So, what that means, is that...well...you know that the brain is encased by the skull and there are holes in the skull in different places. So, what can happen is that when there is increased pressure within the skull cavity or within the brain, like, for example, if there is suddenly a lot of blood in the brain, then the brain tissue itself can actually push, or herniate, through the holes in the skull," I tried to explain by curving my fingers into a circle and pushing my other hand through the makeshift hole. It was graphic and horrific, but...necessary.

"So, the fact that this is happening, and we can see it on the CT scan, is a very ominous sign that he may, in fact, have brain death. The problem is that we can't really know for sure until the medications that he was given when he was put on the breathing machine have worn off, which is going to take several hours."

"OK, so we wait and see then," Ilene said, nodding her head while wringing her hands together. I knew that the only thing they probably heard from my whole dialogue was "we can't really know for sure." But that was ok. They've heard it once and you have to start somewhere.

"Yes, it's going to be wait and see, and in the meantime, I actually already spoke to the neurosurgeons and the interventional radiologists and they are going to talk to you about possibly doing that coiling procedure I explained before," I paused. The looks on their faces made me stop. I could see they could barely remember what I had said just seconds before, which under the circumstances was not surprising at all. I'd say it as many times as I had to, plus I had the benefit of having Chris as an audience, so I could use the opportunity to teach him something too.

"What they do is, they inject some dye into a vein so they can look at the blood vessels in the brain and watch the blood flow. The dye makes a 'road map' of the blood vessels in the brain. They can then see if there is an aneurysm which is what we think may have been the cause of all of this," I began.

"What exactly is an aneurysm?" Ilene asked.

Oye, I thought to myself, feeling bad that I hadn't explained that earlier. After awhile, it's hard to remember which words are "medical" words and which words a non-medical person might understand. Choosing words can be difficult-you don't want to choose medical words, but at the same time, you don't want to sound condescending by simplifying things too much. Families get annoyed either way, but I was lucky that Ilene was smart enough to admit that she didn't understand.

"An aneurysm is like a balloon, or a pouch that forms alongside a blood vessel. It bulges out from a weakness in the side of a blood vessel, and as it bulges, the wall stretches and can rupture. If Walter has an aneurysm, they may be able to thread a coil inside the balloon to plug it up and stop the bleeding. But, again, a coil can't do anything about the damage that's already been done," I told them.

Their heads began nodding and I could see that they understood. I waited for them to wrap their heads around the concept and so I kept quiet while they digested it.

"When are they going to do this procedure?" Jake finally asked.

"As soon as possible, I presume. The interventional radiologist, Dr. Conn will probably come talk to you and get you to sign a consent form and he'll give you the specifics. In the meantime, I'm getting a room ready for him in the ICU," I said, trying to sound reassuring.

"And is this instead of doing surgery?" Ilene asked.

"Well, that's really a question for the neurosurgeons and the radiologists," I hedged. Truthfully, I wasn't sure. I didn't want to mention the possibility of the drain until I knew for sure if Dr. Anteas was going to pursue that route. So, I was grateful when I saw Dr. Anteas enter the room. He was wearing his bright green scrubs, ready for action in the OR if the situation required it. Having him there gave me a tinge of hope. Maybe I was wrong and there was something we could do for Walter. As Dr. Anteas introduced himself to Walter's parents, I glanced back over to Walter's ventilator. Still no extra breaths. Still no signs of life.

"I think I get it now," Chris said as we left the room. We had excused ourselves while Dr. Anteas examined Walter and interviewed his parents.

"Get what?" I asked, realizing I still hadn't really explained anything about what was happening to Chris.

"How he can be dead yet still have a heart beat and a blood pressure," he said.

I smiled. He had probably been pondering this during the whole dialogue that had just happened. It was confusing as hell. "Tell me," I said encouragingly.

"The heart has its own innervation, so even when the brain dies, the heart can still beat. It has automaticity," he said proudly.

"Yep. You got it," I said. "Don't you just love anatomy?"

He chuckled. "Not really."

"I was never very good at anatomy either," I admitted "The fact that the heart has cells capable of generating their own electrical impulses to stimulate a heart beat is pretty amazing. Especially since that means the heart can beat even without a brain. It makes things difficult though. Lay people aren't used to thinking about life and death in terms of anatomy."

"Yeah, I mean, he doesn't look dead," Chris said.

"Well, he probably is, but we'll know for sure soon enough," I said. "In the meantime, I better give Dr. York a call and let him know what's going on."

Dr. York was the ICU attending on tonight. He was the one I ran all the admissions by and he was the one that oversees all my work and decisions. Just as I was overseeing the medical students, interns and residents, Dr. York was overseeing me, right up the chain of command.

"Sounds good," he said as I finished the story. "Well, it sounds awful, but the plan sounds good."

"Right, thanks," I said. I always appreciated some humor amidst these kinds of situations.

"Once the meds wear off, start the brain death protocol," he instructed. "What time do you think the second formal exam will be?"

"Probably early tomorrow morning," I answered, glancing at the wall clock.

The protocol involved two formal neurologic exams without any medications on board, and those exams had to be about eight hours apart. I counted the hours on my fingers. "Around 8 or 9am."

"Alright," Dr. York said. "Let me know if anything changes."

"You got it," I said. "Have a good night. Hopefully I won't talk to you again!"

"Yeah, hopefully not," he answered with a laugh. If we had to speak again, that meant someone was very sick and I needed help or that there was another admission to the unit. When on night call, the less you had to talk to your attending meant the slower the night and the more sleep you got. Unfortunately for Walter, I didn't expect too much to come up.

An hour later, Arvin and I were now back upstairs in the unit reviewing Walter's labs, awaiting his arrival to the unit from IR. His labs were all normal, there was no alcohol or drugs in his system, and so it was looking more and more like this was probably a ruptured aneurysm. Arvin and I were scouring through the computer system to see if Walter had been to our hospital before and if there were any clues to what had happened lurking in his old records. We had just given up when Dr. Anteas came into the unit.

"Any news?" I said when I saw him.

"No," he answered. "He's in IR now. I just came up to check on Mr. Grant while we wait."

Mr. Grant was another a patient who had a head bleed for whom Dr. Anteas had placed a drain into his brain earlier in the day. Mr. Grant had fallen and had blood pooling around the outside of his brain tissue, a subdural hematoma. "Oh. He's been stable all night," I offered.

"Do you think you might take Walter to the OR?" Arvin asked.

"I doubt it," he answered.

"But, isn't it at least something we can try?" Arvin said.

"You know," Dr. Anteas said as he sat on the edge of the computer table with his legs dangling off the side, "there are worse things than dying. Its much easier for us to do the wrong thing, than it is to do the right thing."

It was an interesting statement and I wasn't sure what he meant, but he continued before I could ask.

"If he's not already brain dead, I could take Walter to the OR and drill a hole in his head and place a drain inside his brain and maybe, *maybe*, save his life. Maybe by taking the blood out and the pressure off I might prevent him from herniating to the point of brain death. But, then what? The question you have to ask yourself, is what are you left with and are you prepared to deal with the consequences?"

Arvin and I sat silent.

"I mean, you'll be left with a 29 year old kid, healthy as can be, except he is in a permanent coma. He'll never wake up. He'll never open eyes or say hello to his family, or even know they're there. He'll exist within some institution, a hospital, nursing home, whatever, for the rest of his life. He'll get infections and have a feeding tube. He'll have a rectal tube and a Foley, forever. He'll move only when the nurses turn him. He'll get bedsores. He'll have no quality of life, no awareness. And his family will be left with a son who is alive, but that's it," Dr. Anteas said, his eyes alive with emotion. "So, like I said, there are worse things than dying."

And he was so right.

It wasn't long before we got the call. No flow. There was no blood flow to the brain. On either side. Zero. In a way, it was a blessing. I now had definitive evidence of what we suspected from the very beginning. Walter was dead. He was dead the moment he arrived in the ER, but the fact that his heart continued to beat made the situation...sticky. Not uncertain, but, sticky. There wasn't any doubt that Walter was dead, but the fact that his body was warm, you could feel his pulses and the ventilator made his chest rise up and down with each delivered breath presented a picture of a man in a deep coma, not the picture of a dead man. Our job as the medical team was going to be explaining the difference between brain death and cardiac death to Ilene and Jake Atkins and to tell them that their 29-year-old son, Walter, was already gone.

"Go ahead and call Gift of Life," I instructed Arvin, "I don't know if he's an organ donor or not, but it's time to make the call."

Arvin nodded and dialed. It was too late for Walter, but maybe there was someone who could be saved.

Once Walter's body and his family were settled in the room, I turned to Arvin. Dr. Anteas had gotten called away to another emergency in the ER, and so rather than wait for him to return, I figured we should relay the news.

"Do you want to lead the talk?" I offered.

"Not particularly," Arvin admitted. "I'd rather just listen."

"OK," I said. I should have insisted that Arvin lead the discussion, but the truth was, I wanted to do it myself. I had already started the discussion earlier and so it was probably less confusing for Ilene and Jake if they had one doctor as their point person. "You'll be the one here through the night, though, so you should come with me. They need to get to know you too."

Arvin agreed and we headed towards Walter's new room.

Right before we got to the room I stopped abruptly and turned to Arvin.

"Don't mention organ donation," I told him sternly. "Gift of Life doesn't want the physicians taking care of him to bring it up. They prefer to bring it up themselves."

Arvin nodded. "Yeah, I know."

State law mandates that for every death, the organ donation agency has to be notified, regardless of whether or not the patient was a candidate for organ donation or not. But bringing up the concept of organ donation was not the job of the physicians taking care of the patient, it was the job of the organ donation agency. We had to focus on Walter and his brain, not his healthy organs.

"Hi there," I said as I entered the room. Ilene and Jake were seated by the windowsill. Ilene was talking on her cell phone and Jake was seated quietly, watching the monitors as they displayed Walter's heart rate and blood pressure.

"Oh, I have to go, the doctor's here. I'll call you later," Ilene said into her phone and then abruptly flipped it shut.

"Hi doctor," she said.

"Hi, how are you guys doing?" I said, I walked to Walter's bedside and rubbed his leg gingerly over the blankets. My eyes stayed on Jake and Ilene, trying to gauge how they were coping. Ilene seemed exhausted and her eyes were red with fatigue and tears. Jake was harder to read. He remained the same stoic statue, staring at the ground whenever I tried to meet his eyes.

"I just got the result from the procedure and when they tried to measure the blood flow to Walter's brain, well, I'm really sorry to say that there was not any flow," I paused. "That means that there is no blood going to his brain, which means that he has brain death."

Jake broke down first, burying his head in his hands, moaning and mumbling some words I couldn't understand. Ilene began sobbing and turned her head into Jake's shoulder.

"I'm so sorry," I said. Arvin stood silently next to me and we looked at each other with sad looks, both of us feeling helpless and useless.

To make things worse, I knew I had to bring up "the protocol"." I struggled trying to decide how long to wait before moving the conversation forward into discussions of policy and protocol, but I had to let them know what would happen next. I had to keep them moving forward so they could get on with the inevitable reality that we would be taking away the machines since Walter was dead.

Each hospital has a different policy regarding the declaration of brain death, the mechanics of making that diagnosis and the events that happen after someone is declared brain dead. Legally, I could declare Walter brain dead and fill out his death certificate right now. The result of the flow study combined with the neurologic exam was definitive evidence enough for me to declare Walter dead. Since the flow study is not a test we commonly order, however, the hospital created a policy, "the brain death protocol", to help us dot the I's and cross the T's. The policy was just wishy-washy enough that it left it up to the physician's clinical judgment whether there needed to be an observation period before declaring brain death. There was no blanket statement, no magic formula, but a series of recommendations based on ethical, legal and moral principles established within medical societies.

An observation period during which two full neurologic exams are performed, approximately eight hours apart is sometimes initiated, usually in the absence of other testing. After the second exam, if the exam reveals brain death, the patient is declared deceased. The patient is then removed from the ventilator and in the absence of oxygen, the heart eventually will cease to beat.

In Walter's case, though, I didn't need a protocol. There was no uncertainty here because I had a flow study showing zero blood flow to the brain, but there certainly wasn't much harm in extending the brain death protocol to its final detail. Although an observation period was not necessary in Walter's case, I favored an observation period, as did Dr. York, knowing that the extra time would allow the Atkins' a little extra time to process, grieve and to say goodbye.

And so, against my scientific instincts, I chose not to declare Walter dead, but instead began to explain the "brain death protocol." With Arvin standing solemnly at my side, I told the Atkins that in the morning, around 8 am, Dr. York would arrive and we would all meet together and perform one final exam. If it was consistent with brain death, as we expected it would be, the machines would be removed from Walter's body.

The Atkins continued their tears, burying their faces in each other's arms while Arvin and I meagerly tried to extend our condolences. Words didn't come easy, and so I decided it was time to leave them to begin the process of saying goodbye.

As I turned to leave, there was a sudden unfinished business that bothered me and it stopped me at the door. As Arvin left the room, I hesitated and then turned back towards Walter's parents. "You know, one last thing. I know this is all really hard to hear and I can't even imagine what it feels like to be in your shoes. There is probably very little that I can say that will be helpful to you, and I'm sure, like me, you feel helpless and powerless. But, in a way, with a tragedy like this, having nature make the decisions for you is actually a blessing," I stopped, hoping my words were coming out right. They probably weren't, but I continued anyway.

"At least there isn't a looming decision or a choice for you to make. You don't have to worry about deciding whether or not to turn off the machines. If we declare brain death, well, that's it. You don't have to tell us to take away the ventilator, you don't have to decide. It just will be what it is. In a way, Walter spared you that agony by leaving on his own accord. It may seem like a small detail, but, well, maybe it will give you a little comfort." I looked at Jake. There was no change in his facial expression and Ilene continued to sob. I looked down to my toes, turned and left the room, leaving the clock ticking behind me.

The next morning came with no major events through the night. I had left the unit in Arvin and the other residents' capable hands as the rest of the patients in the unit were relatively stable. I was grateful that I had been able to go home and get some rest. My cell phone and pager had been mercifully quiet with just a few calls and questions from the residents and there weren't any other admissions that arrived for the ICU. I was acknowledging my luck as I dressed in the morning and thought about the day that lay ahead. As long as things remained quiet I would be able to focus my attention on Walter and his family without distractions from other urgent cases. In the ICU, you never know what your day might hold, but I was going to keep my fingers crossed that I'd be able to devote my time to the Atkins.

By the time I made it to Walter's room, Dr. Greenberg, the neurology attending, was examining Walter with Arvin. Jake and Ilene were not there, but I noticed their bags strewn across the window ledge, so I knew they hadn't gone far. Probably to get some coffee. There were crumpled blankets slouched over the chairs in Walter's room, so I presumed they had spent the night at Walter's side.

"Good morning," I greeted as Dr. Greenberg moved Walter's head from side to side, observing his eye movements, or lack thereof.

"Hi," Dr. Greenberg answered, looking up from his exam. "Did you admit him last night?"

I tensed up. Dr. Greenberg wasn't my attending, but I suddenly got nervous that I was about to get ridiculed for admitting a dead man to the intensive care unit and furthermore for keeping his body alive through the night. He was in his mid-fifties and significantly higher up than me in the 'food chain'.

"Yes," I said.

"Have you met the family?" he asked me.

"Yes, I spoke with them for awhile last night," I said, unsure if Dr. Greenberg was upset with me or if he was just being very matter of fact. "I explained the brain death protocol to them late last night, so they sort of know what's going on, but I still think we should review everything with them again, now that's its morning."

"Sure," he said, his tone lifting into a warmer demeanor. Maybe he was happy that the worst part of the job had already been done. His stress level seemed to decrease once he knew that the initial discussion had already been done.

"I'm happy to meet with them too if you'd like. Who is the ICU attending?" he said.

"That would be great," I said, relieved that he wasn't angry. "Dr. York is the attending and I'm going to try to arrange a meeting between him and the family, so if you'd like to come, I'm sure that would be helpful." I always felt that the more different specialists at a family meeting, the better. It made the family feel like we were covering all our bases, and in the situation of brain death, it was probably comforting for them to also hear the dismal news from a neurologist. It wasn't really necessary, considering any physician can diagnose and declare brain death, but I thought it would be a nice touch to have a neurologist to answer any questions the Atkins may have. Particularly since we would be removing the ventilator once the final exam was performed. I was pleased Dr. Greenberg volunteered to be there.

"Just page me when you are meeting and I'll be there," he said. "Did you call Gift of Life?"

"Yeah," I answered, "they're going to talk to the family after we finish the second exam."

"Great. Thanks for taking care of it."

He left the room and Arvin, being a future neurologist, fell into step right behind him, leaving me alone with Walter for the first time. It was hard to see him, so young and so much like me. I thought about his young healthy body with its non-functioning brain and shook away the thoughts of whether Walter's healthy organs might save someone else's life.

When it was time for the meeting, I led the Atkins' into the conference room and they sat down without a word. Since the residents were all still preparing their morning progress notes, I was the youngest doctor in the room and so I said nothing and waited for my seniors to begin the meeting. Dr. York began by introducing himself and Dr. Greenberg and then summarized for the Atkins all the events that had transpired thus far. As he spoke, I let my eyes and thoughts wander. On one side of the conference table sat the Atkins, wearing the same clothing from the night before, looking tired and shattered. I had memorized Jake and Ilene Atkins' stoic faces since we had first met and this morning they looked no different. Now, with Dr. York leading the conversation instead of me, I had a chance to really study the Atkins. They were a timid couple, in fact, they rarely spoke, and I wondered if this was who they were or was it rather their grief disguised as shyness.

On the other side of the table were the three of us doctors, a strange collection of characters, I had to admit. First, there was me, the youngest in the room. I was the only one wearing a white coat, which, in this sort of meeting, I relied upon to serve as a reminder to myself that I was at work, performing a job. I was painfully aware that my age was essentially the same as Walter's and for this I felt like an imposter. My white coat served as a barrier of sorts for me, keeping my emotional self at a distance from the family members seated in front of me.

Then, there was Dr. York, who was in his mid-forties, a young and energetic ICU doctor who dressed the part in his blue scrubs and shaggy hair. As he spoke, his words were cushioned by his experience in critical care and I envied the way the words slid off his tongue. His age put a certain emphasis behind his words and I noticed that the Atkins seemed to listen to him with a different intentness than they did when I had spoken to them, and with that came a different fear.

Lastly, sitting on the end, was the neurology attending, Dr. Greenberg, wearing a three-piece suit. His tie had a silver and blue pattern that popped from his charcoal gray sport coat. He looked more like an outpatient doctor than he did an inpatient doctor, probably because he wasn't wearing his white coat. No doubt he had office hours later on this morning, but the contrast of his attire from Dr. York's and mine' made him stand out in contrast.

As Dr. York finished his recap of events, I noticed the Atkins demeanor begin to change. Maybe it was because hearing the events from Dr. York, who was older and more authoritative looking than me, or maybe because it was their second or third time hearing the terrible truth of Walter's condition, but I began to see their faces change ever so slightly from a state of shock, to a state of grief. Jake Atkins looked over at Dr. Greenberg after Dr. York finished speaking, prompting Dr. Greenberg to speak.

"I agree with everything you just heard," he said, obviously picking up on the Atkins' need for even more confirmation. "I examined your son earlier this morning and he didn't have any of the basic brainstem reflexes that are compatible with life."

Upon hearing the words from Dr. Greenberg, Jake Atkins finally broke down. As he and his wife cried, the three of us on the other side of the table sat quietly and respectfully, patiently waiting for whatever was going to happen next. Silence was important in situations like this, that was lesson number one from medical school yet our silence stood out to me like a flashing light amidst the Atkins' cries and sobs.

Dr. York was the one who finally spoke first.

"We're going to perform the second neurologic exam and based on the result of that exam, we'll then begin the process of removing the machine," he said. "Is there anyone else you'd like to come to the hospital before we do that?"

"No," Ilene managed, her voice high pitched and shaking.

"When you remove the machines, what will happen then?" Jake said, "He just...dies?"

"No, Mr. Atkins," Dr. York said, "he is already dead. When we take away the ventilator, his body will stop getting oxygen and eventually his heart will stop beating. Right now, the heart is still working because we are feeding it with oxygen and it has its own power supply, independent of the brain. But, removing the machine isn't allowing him to die, because he's already gone. The only thing that will change is that his heart will no longer beat."

Jake Atkins looked at all of us as we sat there nodding our heads in agreement. Ilene put her head down on the table, burying her face in her arms. I pitied them watching as they tried to understand how their son's heart could beat yet we were telling them he was already gone. It was confusing even to me and this wasn't the first nor would it be the last brain death case I'd be involved in, but it was equally hard as if it was my first.

Science, religion and philosophy were colliding in my head. How do we define death? What is it to be alive? Why is a beating heart not a sign of life? My instincts nagged me otherwise. I thought about how Chris had been so confused in the ER, and he was a medical student, with medical training. Yet, he had to "figure out" what death meant. Here was the conundrum I had foreseen back when I first viewed Walter's brain images in the ER dreading the task that lie ahead, the task of explaining it all in a way that a family- this family...the Atkins, could understand.

Knowing and believing in science and medicine has always been enough for me and in my medical mind, brain death is just another type of death. Medicine and science have gone to great lengths pinpointing the definition of death. I stretched my mind to try to humanize my definition by taking myself out of the scientific world I live in and morphing it into a more intuitive one. Perhaps, I thought, it might not be enough to simply leave it at that. If it were my husband, or son, or friend, or parent lying in that bed instead of Walter, would I truly feel and believe that he was dead, with his flushed face, warm skin and beating heart?

"But will he feel pain?" Ilene asked as I shook my thoughts to the back of my mind and focused on the room again.

"No, he won't have any pain," Dr. York said. "His brain can't perceive pain."

"When is the next exam?" Jake asked.

Dr. York looked over at me.

"Whenever you're ready," I said.

Dr. York and Dr. Greenberg stood up and offered their hands and final condolences to the Atkins. Jake and Ilene rose as well.

"There's no rush," I assured them as the attendings left the room. "Take all the time you like with Walter and then let the nurse know when you're ready for me to come in and do the exam."

"OK, thank you," Ilene said as she passed me as I held the door open for her and Jake. I waited behind so they wouldn't feel my presence following them to the room. In the meantime, I figured I'd check in with the residents and see how things were going in preparation for morning rounds.

Back in the unit, I searched for my resident teams to see if there was anything I could do to help them get ready for rounds, but they were all scurrying around the unit like a bunch of flies trapped in a jar. Rather than slowing them down, I decided to flip through some of the charts as I waited for my summons from the Atkins. As I opened the first chart, I saw the Gift of Life representative paging through Walter's medical record. I stared at the chart pages as I flipped, not really reading what was written on the pages as they passed. I was too distracted, so it was a relief when I got the summons twenty minutes later from Walter's nurse, Joe, who motioned to me from across the room. It was time.

As I stood over Walter shining my penlight in his eye, I was painfully aware that I was only going through the motions now. The results of the flow study were etched in my mind. There was no blood flowing to Walter's brain. But, I repeated the neurologic exam with Dr. York and Dr. Greenberg chatting softly in the background while I performed the testing. The Atkins had chosen to step outside while I did the final exam. By now, the residents were in radiology rounds reviewing x-rays, so it was just me left to do the exam. I repeated the same maneuvers I had done the evening before, this time with my attending in the room to make it even more official. For completion sake, I even did the cold caloric test, in which I injected cold water into Walter's ears to observe if he had nystagmus, or eye movements in response to the water. I did five or six maneuvers, and all confirmed brain death.

"Time of death, 8:42 am," I said quietly, more for myself so I would remember the time for the death certificate. I took a step back from his bed and looked at my dead patient. It was approximately 15 hours since I had first met Walter, and sadly, nothing had changed since the moment he had arrived except that the Atkins had begun the process of accepting that their son was dead.

We removed the machines ten minutes later. The Atkins had declined organ donation for religious reasons so there was no reason to wait. Dr. York and Dr. Greenberg had moved on to begin their daily rounds, and I was left to withdraw the machines with the nurse and respiratory therapist. The Atkins had decided to stay outside the room while we removed the ventilator, making the process a lot quicker. I didn't have to go through the explanations. Joe, the nurse, suctioned Walter's mouth out to prevent any extra drool or secretions from sliding out along with the ventilator tubing and messing up his hospital gown. As Joe did the suctioning, the respiratory therapist, Nancy, prepared the tube so it would be easily withdrawn by removing the straps and deflating the ventilator cuff. With a swift move, she pulled the tube out of Walter's mouth and Joe did his cleanup with the suction catheter. The ventilator alarms screamed until Nancy was able to reach over and slap the silence button as if it was the snooze button on her alarm clock. The whole process took about 10 seconds and other than the brief alarms, the atmosphere in the room was quiet and somber.

"Can I bring them in?" I asked Joe.

"I'll get them," he answered and slipped out the door, anxious to get out of the room.

I went over to the monitor and looked at its screen. His heart rate was a perfect 70 beats per minute, with the EKG tracing showing a picture perfect rhythm. His blood pressure was equally perfect. His oxygen level read 99%. I reached up and switched off the screen so that when Jake and Ilene came back in the room, they wouldn't see his vital signs. They were just numbers at this point, perfect numbers, in fact, but with no meaning.

The Atkins came in just as I switched off the monitor and the silent room was suddenly filled with tears and sobs. Nancy, Joe and I quietly left the room, to allow them time alone with Walter. We congregated in the nursing station, watching the remote monitor of Walter's vital signs. Without the ventilator, Walter's body had no way of getting oxygen and so his oxygen level had already dropped to 90%. His heart was still beating and we could see that his heart rate and blood pressure had barely changed. I looked through the window leading into Walter's room and saw his mother with her head resting on Walter's chest as she sobbed. Jake wasn't in my view, so I assumed he was seated on a chair further back in the room.

Joe and I sat vigilantly by the monitor, not talking much as we watched Walter's oxygen levels drop. Nancy had already moved on to administer a breathing treatment to another patient in need, but neither Joe nor I had anywhere better to be. So, we just sat and watched as Walter's numbers gradually crept from perfect to less so. His heart rate slowed and his blood pressure dropped until finally, his heart stopped altogether. It took about fifteen minutes from the time we took the ventilator away until his heart stopped completely.

"I guess I should go check on them," I said to Joe.

"Yeah," he said, "let me know if they need anything."

As I opened the door to Walter's room, his mom lifted her head from Walter's chest and turned towards me.

"He's gone, isn't he?" she wailed.

I hesitated, holding back the urge to reinforce the fact that he had gone long ago, but that the electrical energy of the heart had stopped. But I knew that the beating heart was far too symbolic of life to explain away with science.

"Yes, his heart just stopped beating," I answered instead.

"I know," she cried, "I heard it. I heard the whole thing. I heard it when it stopped."

Jake Atkins held his head low, crying full, wet tears. And for just a moment, I too felt what Jake and Ilene Atkins felt- that Walter had died just then, just in that moment, with the silencing of his heart.

"We're all outside if you need anything," I managed to say, surprised at my own thoughts as I backed out the door, retreating into the unit and back into the world of science and medicine.

Chapter Five: Victoria's Story

I T ALL STARTED with a sneeze. Sitting on her porch, comforted by her rocking chair, Victoria sneezed three times in rapid fire. She looked over to the blossoms dangling from the tree just to her right and sighed. The allergies were back and she knew she'd better go inside and lie down. The same thing happened yesterday and she didn't want her throat to close up like that again. Victoria had lived in her house for a long time and always enjoyed a quiet afternoon on the porch, but over the last few months, she couldn't stay outside for very long before her allergies started to act up. "I'm too old for this", she thought, not understanding the truth behind what she was thinking. In reality, 79-year-old women don't suddenly develop allergies. But, Victoria was a strong woman, a healthy woman, who didn't even fathom that there could be anything else wrong.

Once inside her house, she shooed the cat off the sofa and laid down for a quick nap. Victoria kept a tidy home and things were always in their correct place. There was not a speck of dust to be found in Victoria's home and the only shred of clutter rested on her mantle that was teaming with ornately framed photographs of her children and grandchildren. There were 8 frames in all and each frame contained a portrait of her respective daughters and sons with their children. There were forty smiling faces peering out from their frames, looking over her as she slept.

But after a few hours, her allergies were getting worse, despite the fact that she had been indoors for quite some time. The breathlessness was increasing and she didn't feel like herself. She lifted the phone and called 911; she needed some strong allergy medicine and she needed it soon. She felt a little silly, bringing in paramedics for an old lady with an allergy attack, but she didn't know what else to do. After the call she went upstairs to put on her new blouse and slacks. She tied the laces on her black leather shoes and went downstairs to wait for the paramedics to arrive. She was surprised at how exhausted she was just after changing her clothes and the flight of stairs, but she felt better once she was back on the sofa. She picked up her knitting to distract herself while she sat in her quiet house. Gosh, she hated hospitals- all the noise and all the fuss. Her cat purred beside her and Victoria made a mental note to pick up some cat food on her way back home.

The result of the x-ray was back about thirty minutes later. The doctor was young and handsome, but Victoria couldn't pronounce his name. All she knew was that he had just told her she had cancer.

Victoria's daughter, Lana was driving to the hospital a few hours later. She had just received a call from her mother asking her to come to the hospital. Mom had sounded pretty calm on the phone so Lana knew that it wasn't that bad. Lana knew her mother had been suffering from terrible allergies and she was certain that her mom would tell her she had pneumonia. She just hoped it wasn't too debilitating. Victoria was so independent and Lana knew her mom didn't take well to being sick. Mom had the tendency to try and do more than she could handle and so Lana would have to keep a close eye on her to make sure she didn't overextend herself. If Mom was sick, Lana knew it was going to be up to her to take care of her. Not that she minded, but it wasn't exactly part of her master plan. Work was getting busier by the day and she didn't need the added stress of trying to convince her Mom to go to doctors' appointments. Mom hated doctors and hospitals so Lana would have to be vigilant to make sure she kept up with whatever medical care this illness required. Lana knew she'd have to take charge, and she would.

Dr. Chelsea Olson was reading in the resident's lounge around the same time Lana was driving to the hospital. Her beeper went off and Chelsea's heart sank.

There it was. It was now going to be at least a few hours before she could sit down again, let alone read, and she knew it. Chelsea was the resident on call for all new intensive care unit evaluations, and her pager was beeping. The phone was across the room, so it was time to get off the sofa and spring into action. She answered the call, knowing full well that it was Dr. Fred Bernstein, the intensive care fellow. He was her boss tonight and he would be calling her if there were a patient who needed to be evaluated. There was. She was on the 17th floor: a lady with shortness of breath and some kind of cancer. Chelsea tried to hide the annoyance in her voice as she assured Fred she'd see the patient right away. Once the phone was back on its cradle, Chelsea put down her book, wrapped her stethoscope around her neck and set off for the 17th floor.

The nurse, who was anxiously awaiting the doctor's arrival, greeted Chelsea at the door and told her that Victoria seemed more short of breath over the last few hours and that she was now on the maximum amount of oxygen that her nose tube could emit. Chelsea nodded and sat down at the nursing station with the chart, which was mercifully thin. It wasn't exactly the reading she wanted to be doing right now, she thought. She opened the chart and began to read. The story was pretty typical: a newly diagnosed ovarian cancer with spread to the lungs. The patient had presented with complaints of an "allergy attack". How bad could this shortness of breath really be then? Maybe she could finish her book after all. The oncologists were evaluating whether she was a surgical candidate and whether she would require chemotherapy. Chelsea couldn't really read the oncologist's handwriting, but it didn't matter. She was here to assess the patient's shortness of breath and see whether she needed to be moved to intensive care. Once she gathered the story from the chart, she headed to the room to meet Victoria.

Victoria was in the room at the end of the hall, the nicest one on the wing because it had a large window overlooking the picnic area. In a way, it seemed cruel, Chelsea thought, allowing the patients to see all the healthy people eating their lunches outside in the perfect weather whilst they were trapped in their hospital beds...although she knew that the light and the window in itself could be healing. Chelsea was thinking about the window when she walked in the room and found Victoria sitting in the chair beside her hospital bed.

Immediately upon seeing Victoria, Chelsea transformed into Dr. Olson and all thoughts of the resident's lounge vanished. With each breath, Victoria's neck muscles contracted violently and it took her two full syllables to say "hel"-gasp-"lo". This wasn't an allergy attack. This was a woman in severe respiratory distress. Dr. Olson surveyed the room. Victoria's vital signs were displayed on the monitor: heart rate was fast, breathing was fast, but her blood pressure was ok. The oxygen saturation was at 90%. That was bad. On full nasal oxygen she was *only* at 90%. Chelsea called for the nurse to get a non-rebreather mask which is capable of delivering 100% oxygen. She felt her own heart rate start to rise as she contemplated where to start and what to do next.

And then, Chelsea was stopped dead in her tracks. It was Victoria's eyes. They were calm. They were so calm, despite the fact that she was breathing at a rate twice as fast as a normal person would breath. Suddenly and without warning, Chelsea was calm too. She was struck by the serenity that Victoria exuded and the lack of fear on her face so much that Chelsea's own fears and insecurities seemed to melt away. She sat on the bedside next to Victoria and introduced herself. With all the chaos that was going on around poor Victoria, Chelsea wanted to be certain that Victoria knew who she was and what her role was.

"I'm Dr. Olson and I am one of the residents working in the intensive care unit tonight. Your doctors asked me to come evaluate you because you are having such a hard time breathing, so I'm here to see if I can help you," she said.

Victoria nodded in understanding and managed a feeble smile at the young doctor before her.

Chelsea sat on the bed next to Victoria's chair and listened as Victoria tried between gasps to tell her how her shortness of breath was getting worse and worse, that she felt like she was suffocating. The words were slow and it was a great effort for Victoria to get them out of her lips, but Chelsea listened patiently, encouraging Victoria to take her time in telling her what she wanted her to know.

As Chelsea listened, somewhere in the deep recesses of her brain, something familiar about Victoria was haunting her. At first she couldn't quite place what it was until a few minutes into the conversation, but once the thought popped into her consciousness, she couldn't quite shake it. The calm way in which Victoria was laying out what had happened to her, the pragmatic and articulate nature in which she described the past horrifying hours, it was exactly the way her own mother would have told it had it been Mom in Victoria's chair. They were both calm in ways that she was not and the familiarity Victoria exuded was palpable.

Chelsea had just returned from a weeklong trip home to California where she had spent some long overdue quality time with her mother. Chelsea's mother was her rock, her best friend, and this Northeastern hospital was about as far away from her as Chelsea could stand. Especially right now. Whenever Chelsea came back from a trip home she felt the distance between her and her family like a thick blanket, and the similarity that Victoria bore to Chelsea's mother that tugged at her heart. "I have to do this right," Chelsea said silently.

By the time she had finished, Victoria could barely complete a sentence. Chelsea knew there wasn't much time before her lungs tired out and she would require a ventilator to stay alive. She needed to see the x-ray. She strongly suspected a cancer-related pleural effusion, fluid in the lung that can easily be removed. She stepped outside to the x-ray computer and pulled up the films.

Chelsea stared. She couldn't believe what she was seeing. There was no fluid. It was like a tumor gun had been aimed at Victoria's lungs and the trigger was pulled releasing a rapid succession of tumor bullets all over her lung fields. It was incredible. It was unlike anything she had ever seen. But, worst of all, one of the many tumors was obstructing a bronchus. This was far from an easy fix. There was no fluid she could remove. This was a huge tumor, a tumor that would kill Victoria...and it would kill her soon.

After Chelsea got over the shock of the severity of her x-ray, she paged Fred to update him about her evaluation of Victoria. She was eager to hear Fred's suggestions about what she should do as Fred had much more experience than she did.

Fred was rounding in the intensive care unit but put all that on hold once he heard Chelsea's story. "I think we need to intubate her now, Fred" Chelsea had told him, trying to sound confident when in fact she had never made that decision on her own before. With that, Fred had hung up the phone, ran up the 3 flights of stairs separating him from Chelsea and arrived huffing.

Chelsea had never worked directly with Fred before. He was a new pulmonary fellow, but Chelsea had heard pretty good things about him. Chelsea was going to specialize in cardiology so all this pulmonary stuff was a little intimidating to her. On her exams, pulmonary wasn't high up on her list of 'excellent performance' subjects. She got by, but preferred arrhythmias and heart attacks to tumors and pneumonias. Her favorite page to receive was the patient in rapid atrial fibrillation with a blood pressure in the toilet. Reading EKG's were a breeze. Those little squiggles were like music in her head. She knew how to defibrillate, or shock, a patient without blinking an eye. Cardiac patients posed no problems for Chelsea, but she couldn't help but feel uneasy, knowing she had never had to make the decision to intubate a patient like Victoria before. So when

Fred arrived, she felt better. She would be relying on Fred to ensure everything went smoothly.

The next five minutes set everything in motion. Chelsea reached Victoria's daughter, Lana, on her cell phone (amazingly, despite all her shortness of breath, Victoria was able to recall this number without hesitation) while Fred reviewed the chart. Lana said she was fifteen minutes away from the hospital and that made both Chelsea and Fred heave a sigh of relief. They all knew that if they did end up putting Victoria on the ventilator, she would probably never come off. Ever. They wanted to hold off as long as possible to allow Lana to be able to speak to her mom before they induced the artificial coma she would require to keep her pain free while on the ventilator. It would probably be the last time Lana ever spoke to her mother, and since she was that close to the hospital, it meant that they could wait.

Karen was in Victoria's room hooking up the non-rebreather oxygen mask. Karen was an experienced nurse, she had been working the cancer ward for twenty something years and she knew what was about to happen. Luckily, her other four patients were all stable at the moment, so she could devote all her time to helping with the situation that was about to go down in Victoria's room. What was taking the doctors so long? Why hadn't they called for a bed in the intensive care unit yet? The female doctor had been here almost twenty minutes and still no one had called in the transfer. She had been up all night trying to help Victoria breathe easier, but nothing she had tried helped. They had done breathing treatments, increased the oxygen in the nasal mask, changed her positioning in the bed, but nothing had worked. That's when she had called the intern, who had called for the unit evaluation. It seemed like an awful long chain of command to her, but that was what a teaching hospital was all about. Call the interns first; they'll call their senior residents who will call the fellows who will call the attendings who were at on call from home. She had worked at non-teaching hospitals before, but she actually preferred the teaching hospitals. More doctors around. True, they were younger and inexperienced, but they were right there, in house.

The oxygen rushed into the mask with a 'whoosh' once Karen flipped the switch. Karen stepped outside to Victoria's room to see what plan the two doctors had conjured. She met them standing just outside Victoria's doorway.

"When are you going to move her?" asked Karen.

"Not yet, we need to stabilize her first," answered Chelsea, sensing the panic in the nurse's voice.

"So, you're just going to wait for her to code?" Karen retorted in disgust.

Chelsea was relieved when Fred answered for her.

"She's ok for now- let's give the non-rebreather a chance to get her oxygen up and then we'll move her to the unit," he said.

Karen spun on her heels and walked back into the room. She had to get this patient off the floor. They weren't equipped here to deal with the level of care this patient needed. The sooner they got her off the floor, the better. Victoria was getting worse by the minute and the transfer process and paperwork was lengthy.

By now, other nurses were arriving to check out the scene and Chelsea felt a strong sense of "us versus them". She could hear the words of the nurses standing around the floor: "She needs to go to the unit *now*" and "You've got to be kidding, they haven't called in the bed yet?" and other such comments were buzzing around the ward like a fly you can't quite see, but know is there. Chelsea felt a lump in her throat. Maybe they were right, they should move her right then and there, but the thought of wheeling a patient across the hospital while she was in distress didn't sit right with Chelsea. Just get the oxygen in her and hope she stabilizes. Then we'll move her. She opened her mouth to discuss things with

Fred, but he was already sitting next to Victoria with her hand in his. Chelsea followed Fred's lead and went back into the room. She joined them in mid-conversation.

"It just came on suddenly, doctor," Victoria was saying, "I feel like I'm suffocating now!"

"Ok, we can help you with that. Dr. Olson has called your daughter and she's on her way. We're going to get you to intensive care, ok?" Fred answered.

"I just feel like I'm suffocating" Victoria said.

As Victoria explained her symptoms to Fred, Chelsea watched the oxygen monitor. It was rising! Slowly, but it was going up! Thankfully, they didn't need to intubate her this instant, although, she knew it was imminent and they were far from out of the woods. Fred's eyes were also on the monitor. He gave Chelsea a quick nod and stood up.

"Get a blood gas and I'll call her in," he said on his way out of the room. This was code for "let's hope they have a bed available in the intensive care unit". Chelsea was amazed at how relaxed Fred seemed to be and she couldn't help but feel envious.

Karen was flitting around the room, packing up Victoria's belongings in large plastic bags. Chelsea felt annoyed. The nurse's priority it seemed was to get rid of this patient just as soon as possible. Chelsea's priority was to stabilize her. Nursing relations were always a challenge, especially when the team had different priorities. They needed just a few minutes to monitor Victoria and get the blood work so they knew exactly what they were dealing with. It was difficult enough to get an arterial blood gas without having the added pressure of the nurse trying to wheel the patient out the door at lightening speed.

"Do you feel any better?" Chelsea asked Victoria. Her oxygen level was now 93%.

Victoria nodded.

"I'm going to have to get an arterial blood gas now," she said. "Do you know what that is?"

Victoria shook her head.

"Its just like a regular blood test, except I won't use a tourniquet and I get the blood out of this artery here, rather than the vein," she explained, as she pointed to her own wrist.

Chelsea was a pretty good stick, but even so, arterial blood gases hurt. The artery is covered in nerves that the needle has to push through to get the blood, whereas the vein has no nerves, so it hurts less. Chelsea left this part out of her explanation. The arterial blood gave more information about oxygen levels than the venous blood did, so there wasn't really much of a choice. She had to do it. She had to know how bad it really was.

Chelsea asked Karen if there was a blood gas kit in the room and Karen handed it to her without a word. The hostility was tangible and Chelsea had to push it from her mind. She had to get the blood. She opened the kit and swabbed down Victoria's wrist with alcohol. She felt for the pulse, counted to three and stuck. Victoria didn't even flinch. The blood flashed into the syringe and within two seconds, it was all over. Chelsea breathed a sigh of relief that she had the precious blood gas.

"Can we move her now?" Karen asked.

"Fred is calling for a bed," Chelsea replied as she taped up Victoria's wrist and left the room.

At the nursing station, Fred had the phone to his ear and scribbled something on a piece of paper for Chelsea to read.

"Bed 1271" it read.

Chelsea was about to go tell the nurse that they had a bed in the unit, but just as she turned, she saw Victoria's bed come wheeling into the hallway. Karen was on her cell and apparently, the nursing supervisor had already told her the news. With a shrug, Chelsea followed her patient down the hall.

By the time Victoria was in her new room and settled, Lana had arrived. Chelsea, Fred and Lana were standing in the central nursing station in the intensive care unit now. Beeps and chirps of ventilators and machines filled the room. Lana looked around the unit. It was a stark contrast from Victoria's previous floor, which was quiet and serene. Here, the noise was thick in the air with shrill sounds and alarms that no one seemed to hear but her. The nursing station was filled with monitors and computers that looked like a command station. The glass walls revealed the patients in their rooms, affording little to no privacy. Bright red metallic emergency carts sat poised outside the rooms, ominously waiting to be used. The sterility of the unit struck Lana, but it was the strange noises that caught her off guard as she entered.

Lana felt very disoriented as she saw her mom lying in a bed through the glass window, wearing a mask that covered her face. She hadn't even had a moment to say hello to her before the doctors had pulled her aside because they wanted to talk to her. Lana felt overwhelmed.

Chelsea and Fred knew it was time for the talk, the "code status" talk. Chelsea had briefed Lana about the cancer, but he still wasn't sure how much Lana *understood* about her mother's condition, so they started simply: they asked her.

"All I know is that 3 weeks ago the only problem she had was that she was more tired than usual and now, she told me she was diagnosed with ovarian cancer that has spread to her lung," Lana said.

"I think we should start by looking at her x-ray" Fred said as he motioned Lana and Chelsea over to the x-ray computer.

Lana followed. She had no idea how to read an x-ray and she was afraid she wouldn't understand what the doctors were showing her. She didn't say anything though, and politely followed behind the doctors.

The computer loaded the film and Lana's hands rocketed up to cover her mouth and she let out a loud gasp that startled Chelsea. "Oh my god!" she yelled. Lana didn't know what she was looking at, but she knew that it was a big, white, round ball smack dab in the middle of her mom's x-ray. Smaller, irregular ones were all over the lungs.

Lana didn't know how to 'read' an x-ray, but it didn't matter. You didn't have to go to medical school to read this one. "I had no idea it was this bad" said Lana. "No idea." Fred paused to let Lana compose herself. "As you can see," he started, "there is more tumor here than there is lung." Lana was silent. "But this one, this big ball here, *this* is the problem."

Lana's eyes naturally fell upon Chelsea, whose head was tilted to the side with sympathy. The sadness in Lana's eyes made Chelsea feel two inches tall. Chelsea knew Lana could understand the picture in front of her and she searched for words to comfort her, but none came.

Fred explained to Lana the happenings of the last hour and pointed to the mass one more time, tracing it with his finger.

"This is *terminal* cancer, isn't it" Lana asked, looking over at Chelsea who nodded. "This is going to kill her."

Chelsea was amazed at how quickly Lana understood and how effective Fred's technique of showing the x-ray had been. They had forgone the long conversation about obstructions and airways and lung tissue. It was all in the picture and simple words could not have done explained the situation better. Lana *got* it. She understood. Fred hadn't said much, but Chelsea felt that the three of them were all on the same level, the same page, and now, it was time to make the decisions.

"Let's go talk with her" Fred said as he led the way back into Victoria's new room.

She's getting worse, thought Chelsea. Victoria's calm had grown into a panic. Her eyes were wide open and she was gasping through the non-breather mask. The blood gas had come back and her oxygen level was very low. The mask was failing and it was time to put her on a breathing machine. Lana was already at her mother's side. She knew that Chelsea was the junior one of the two doctors, but for some reason, she kept looking to Chelsea for answers.

"We have a few options at this point," said Chelsea, directing her words at both Lana and Victoria. "Obviously, she is very short of breath and the mask isn't working well enough. The next step from here is to put a tube down into your lungs and hook you up to the breathing machine," Chelsea said delicately.

"Ok! Get the tube!" gasped Victoria. There was a new desperation in her voice that caught Chelsea off guard.

"I can get the tube," started Chelsea, "but you have to understand that if we put the tube in, it will probably never be able to come out. I need you to understand that," she paused. "And- you won't be able to speak."

"Get the tube!" gasped Victoria. Her eyes were wild and her voice unsteady.

Fred was concerned. The problem was that he knew from the chart that no one had discussed what Victoria's wishes were prior to this moment. And this was the *wrong* moment. Victoria couldn't make sound decisions in her state of air hunger. The next few moments were critical- Fred had to figure out what they would do *after* they put her on the machine. How long would Victoria want to be kept alive on a machine? Would she want them to perform CPR if her heart stopped? Would she want to be kept alive artificially? Would she want them to surgically place a feeding tube, since she wouldn't be able to eat once on the breathing machine? Or, would she want to be made comfortable, forgoing the intubation and the respirator? Would she prefer to be placed on medicine to calm her air hunger, but would certainly mean she would die in the next few hours? These were questions that Fred couldn't ask this woman in this state. It was already far too late.

"Get the tube!" gasped Victoria again.

Lana's eyes were steady though she was fighting back tears. She had to be strong for her mother. She had to keep her composure. This was neither the time nor the place to cry. She had to make sure that whatever was about to happen that she remained in control.

"Do you understand that you won't be able to tell us what your wishes are once we put you on the ventilator?" Chelsea asked, not realizing that she was actually shouting. The panic in Victoria's eyes made it obvious that the real Victoria, the calm Victoria was slipping away. Chelsea shook thoughts of her own mother out of her head. She had to focus on this panic stricken woman and get the answers to her questions. She looked over at Fred, who just stared. They both knew this was not an ideal situation to be discussing code status.

Victoria's hand reached up to Lana.

"You tell them what I want. You do it," panted Victoria as her hand dropped back down onto the bed from the exhaustion of the sentence.

Lana knew that her mom was finished talking. She knew what her mother was asking her to do. It was 'to suffocate', or 'not to suffocate'. That was it. It was not about ventilator machine or no machine. It was more primitive than that. Her mother did not want to die this way; she did not want to suffocate. She wanted air. She wanted to breathe.

Victoria was becoming restless and desperate and Lana realized that she had missed the window of opportunity to discuss with her mom about whether she would want to be sustained on life support. But right now, in this instant, Lana's first priority was to calm her mom, to make her more comfortable and to help her to relax.

She looked at her mother and swallowed: "Alright, Mom. We're getting the tube."

Chelsea stood there in awe as she watched Victoria give her life over to Lana. It was terrifying and beautiful. Fred also saw the transfer, which in his medical mind, was that Victoria had just made Lana her "surrogate". Lana was now the decision maker.

"Please, help her breathe" Lana said to Chelsea and Fred. "She is so uncomfortable. She needs to be peaceful and rest. Let's put her on the machine so she can be calm, and then we can decide later what we want to do,"

With a nod, Fred spun around, poked his head out of the room and asked the nearest nurse to prepare for an emergent intubation.

Once Victoria was on the ventilator, Lana felt a huge sigh of relief. The emergency was over. Her mother was breathing. Well, sort of. But at least she wasn't gasping. She was under sedation with a tube in her mouth that was connected to an enormous mysterious box, the ventilator. Lana had time now. She had time to figure this out.

She headed for the family waiting area and collapsed with a sigh into one of the chairs. She reached into her purse and pulled out her cell phone, not sure which one of her seven siblings to call first. She knew Sara would have the hardest time with the news that Mom was on life support, being the youngest and also the closest to Mom. She dialed her oldest brother first and the phone chain began from there. Within a few hours, the entire family was on their way to the hospital. They were a large group and Lana didn't know how everyone would react. Lana always thought of her family more of a cast of characters than as a close-knit family. They all had their own personalities, their own lives, their own interests, so gathering everyone together under such a devastating condition was a situation that filled Lana with angst. How would she get everyone to come together? What would she say? What if they started arguing? How could she control the situation? Would they be able to unite as a family and make a single, coherent decision? Lana was doubtful and put her head in her hands as she waited for their arrival.

Sara was the first to arrive and Lana was thankful that she intercepted her before she was able to see Victoria on the ventilator. Lana knew she had to prepare Sara for what she was going to see. She had to slow her down, to get her rational, and Sara arrived disheveled, obviously having rushed out the door when she had heard of the intubation. After a few quick hugs and an update, Lana took Sara inside the ICU to see their mom. It was just the two of them and Lana wondered just how many times she'd have to intercept family members to prepare them for what they would see.

Victoria was the figurehead of their family, the single unifying theme. She was pragmatic and strong, never vulnerable. But now, sedated on the medications and intubated, she had the fragility of a porcelain doll. It was hard to prepare for and even harder to see. Lana had to relive the agony of seeing her mother so vulnerable with every new arrival.

Finally, after the entire family had gathered, Fred and Chelsea approached Lana about holding a family meeting, one in which they could explain the recent events to the masses of family members that had gathered in the waiting room. Lana was relieved that someone else was going to do the explaining and together, Lana, Fred and Chelsea herded the group into the family conference room.

The room, although spacious, seemed to collapse under the weight of the forty some family that had gathered there. Despite their enormous numbers, the silence was deafening in the room as the last of the family filed in. Lana, Sara, Chelsea and Fred were the only ones to sit while the rest of the family stood crowded around Lana and Sara in a group. It was the oldest and the youngest, flanked by all those in between.

Chelsea looked around the room and saw one tear streaked face after the next until her eyes fell upon Lana, who remained calm and pragmatic, the new figurehead and the obvious leader of the group. Fred began.

"Thank you all for coming here," he said, "I know this is really hard. It's really wonderful to see everyone coming together, I'm not sure we've ever had a group this large in here before." Soft chuckles broke out throughout the room.

"As I guess you all know by now," he continued, "Victoria has terminal cancer, and earlier today, we had to place her on the ventilator in order to help her breathe, and its unlikely at this time that she will be able to come off because of the amount of tumor that is obstructing her air tube."

He paused. Chelsea's eyes surveyed the room once more and saw nothing but stillness.

"We need to make some decisions about where to go from here, but since there are so many of you, I first want to make sure that we are all on the same page about who is going to be the main decision maker," Fred continued. He looked cautiously at Lana, hoping that the group knew that Lana had already assumed the responsibility.

"Yes," Lana said, "we've already established that I am going to be the voice of the group, that I will be the decision maker, but I'm going to be discussing everything with all the siblings." Heads nodded in agreement.

"Good. That is exactly what we'd like to happen. We want everyone to speak their mind and be involved, but we do need to assign someone as the decision maker, and it was pretty clear that your mom wanted you, Lana, to do that," Fred said. Chelsea nodded as Fred spoke and Lana looked to her and gave a faint smile.

"From here, we have to make decisions about how aggressive we are going to be regarding her care. First, she has an incurable cancer. I know you all understand that, right?" Fred asked.

Heads nodded and some quiet sobs could be heard from the back.

"We need to first make a decision about her code status," Fred began.

"There are several different levels of care that we can offer here, so let me go through them one by one," Fred continued. "First, we can do 'Full Care', in which we would do everything we possibly can to keep your mother alive, including the ventilator, CPR, electric shocks, lines, medications to maintain her blood pressure- basically whatever she would need. That would be the most aggressive option,"

Chelsea looked around to try and get a feel of what the crowd thought of the "full care" option. There weren't many clues in their faces and Chelsea hoped that their lack of head nodding meant that they didn't want to pursue that route.

"Second, we can make her a DNR," Fred continued, "which means that we would maintain her on the ventilator and treat her with medicines, but defer CPR if the need arises and if her heart were to stop, we would let her go peacefully. CPR, as you might not know, can be very violent and it's not uncommon for CPR to cause ribs to break. In someone like your mom, I'm not sure CPR would be a good idea since her cancer is not something we can reverse."

"Next, we can opt for 'Maintenance Care,' which is essentially letting things maintain the course we are on now, without adding anything new to her treatment regimen. We would continue her on the ventilator, but not add any new medications, like pressors to maintain her blood pressure if it were to drop. We would just stay where we are now and see where it leads."

"Finally, we have the option of 'Withdraw of Life Support,' which is when we would start a morphine drip to keep her pain free and comfortable, then take the ventilator off and allow nature to take its course," Fred said.

It was at this point in the speech that Chelsea saw the stoic faces begin to react to the information. Twisted faces and tears filled the room whilst arms came from seemingly nowhere to embrace each other. Sara leaned onto Lana, who kept her eyes on Chelsea, whose facial expression kept her at ease. Lana felt that Chelsea was in her head, comforting her silently and she knew she would be there to help her face the decisions that loomed.

"We will need a little time to discuss it, I think," Lana said, her eyes now on Fred. She didn't want to hold up the doctors and knew that there was a lot of discussion to be had.

"By all means, take your time," Fred answered, "and if you have any questions, Dr. Olson and I will be in the unit."

Lana nodded as Chelsea and Fred stood to leave.

"Thank you, doctors," said a quivering voice from the crowd.

Chelsea lingered for a moment before leaving the room with Fred. She felt awkward leaving Lana behind. She paused before she left.

"I'll be right outside if you have any questions," she said, looking straight at Lana.

"Ok. Thank you," Lana said.

Chelsea slipped out of the room and the door clicked quietly behind her. Sobs erupted as she walked away from the meeting room, and she headed back to the unit to sit and wait for their decision.

Forty-five minutes passed before Lana made her way back into the ICU to look for Dr. Olson. Lana found her sitting behind the desk at the nurse's station. Chelsea rose when she saw Lana enter the unit and met her as she approached.

"How are you?" Chelsea asked, the concern in her voice real and sincere.

"I'm actually ok," Lana said. "We just have to take what comes, I guess."

"I'm so sorry you are in this situation," Chelsea told her.

"Thank you. It's very hard, but I feel like Mom is getting good care and I cannot thank you enough for that. I can really tell that you care about us and it means a lot to me," Lana told her.

Chelsea reached out and touched Lana's arm to show her sincerity as she said, "You are most welcome. Your mother happens to remind me of my own mother, and so it's especially hard for me to watch everything that is happening. I really feel for you and want to help in any way I can."

The two women stood in a silent bond for a few seconds before Chelsea asked, "What has your family decided?"

"We want to give it a few days and see how she does on the ventilator. My sister is hoping that she might wake up a little and be able to communicate with us once she settles down on the ventilator. She is really not ready to take her off the ventilator, although some of my other siblings are leaning in that direction. But, we decided that for now, we'd like to keep the machine going," Lana said.

"That's perfectly reasonable," Chelsea replied, "Have you decided about what level of care you would like, however? Meaning, do you want us to resuscitate her if her heart were to stop?"

"We talked about that too, and we decided she would want to be a DNR and so that's what we're going to do. We'd like to take things as they come, but no, we don't want her to have to undergo CPR or shocks, or anything dramatic like that. If her heart stops, just let her pass," Lana said, her words strong and resolute.

"I'll make a note of that in the chart. We'll keep the ventilator going, but will not perform CPR or shocks. It would also be helpful for me to know what your long term goals are, so that I know how to react if her blood pressure drops or if her oxygen levels were to drop," Chelsea said, her mind racing through all the foreseeable possibilities. She wanted to be absolutely sure that she knew what Lana and her family wanted should something happen in the middle of the night.

"Well, I know this isn't ever going to get better, but my hope is that maybe she might get her to the point where she can hear us, or even communicate with us, if that is even possible," Lana said.

"Of course. We'll do our best to try and make that happen," Chelsea told her, although she wasn't particularly hopeful that they would be successful. "We'll take it one day at a time. Remember, you can always change your mind later and we can revisit this if need be."

"Alright, thanks," Lana said. With a satisfied smile, she then went in to sit by her mother's side.

Five days later, Chelsea popped her head into Victoria's room to give her a quick 'eyeball'. Chelsea's intern had written the daily note and Chelsea had not yet had a chance to do her daily check on Victoria's condition. She was happy to find Lana at the bedside, but was taken aback at how upset she looked.

"Hi," she said trying to mix cheer and empathy into her voice, "how are you doing?"

Lana wiped her emotions from her face and answered, "I'm ok. She just looks awful!" Over the last five days, Victoria hadn't even opened her eyes, let alone communicated with anyone. She hadn't given any sign that she had any awareness of their presence and that had been devastating to the whole family.

Lana paused to look at her mother before continuing. "She's becoming so frail and wasted and her eyes are sunken. She is looking worse and worse every day."

Chelsea knew that this might be Lana's turning point and could tell by the look on her face that the decision to take Victoria off the ventilator was beginning to surface.

"You're right," Chelsea agreed, keeping her voice even and soft "she is becoming very wasted, but the good news is that hemodynamically, she is quite stable. She is tolerating the ventilator well and she's not getting any worse, at least."

"But she's not getting any better, is she?" Lana asked, already knowing the answer.

"No," Chelsea said apologetically.

"I just think she has fought so hard and she looks so tired," Lana said. "It's so tough to see her looking like this."

Chelsea said nothing, but tilted her head in a way that encouraged Lana to continue talking.

"It's been really hard for my sister Sara; she was really close to Mom. And Sara will never be able to say 'stop', although I know that is what she is thinking," Lana said.

"What is it that you think," Chelsea asked, "Regardless of what the rest of your family thinks, you first have to make up your own mind about what you think you should do."

Without hesitation, Lana said, "I think she is too tired and it's time for her to rest. She has put in a hard fight, but look at her! She wouldn't want this, she wouldn't want to live the rest of her life on the ventilator."

"So, you feel like we should withdraw the ventilator?" Chelsea asked, conscious of the fact that she was uttering the words that most families have such a hard time saying.

"Yes, I do," Lana said evenly.

"And you are worried that Sara is going to have a hard time agreeing to it?" Chelsea prompted.

"Exactly," Lana sighed.

Chelsea stayed silent and the women stood surrounded by the humming of the ventilator as it pushed breath into Victoria's diseased lungs.

It was Lana who broke the silence. "I'm going to talk to the family after lunch today, and try to get an idea of where everyone is. But I'm pretty sure that the family is coming to terms with the fact that Mom is fighting a losing battle."

"Well, this is just a different way to look at it, but perhaps if she passes with the whole family with her, perhaps that is a way in which she can win," Chelsea suggested.

Lana shook her head in agreement and let out a soft sigh.

"I'll be right outside if you need me," and Chelsea slid quietly out of the room.

It was time a few hours later. Lana had gathered the family in the waiting area and was waiting for Fred to come outside and give them the 'ok' to come into the unit. There were nearly 40 of them, so the unit had to make some special preparations to accommodate everyone at once. They moved all the unnecessary equipment and waste bins outside of the room and cleared an area outside of Victoria's room for the 'overflow' of people. They had pushed the ventilator and IV poles as close to the wall as they could, to allow for the most people to fit in the room.

Fred emerged from the double doors and they whooshed shut behind him.

"We're ready for you now," he said to Lana.

"Ok. Thank you, doctor, for letting all of us come in to be with her," Lana said appreciatively. She was well aware that in the unit, only two visitors were allowed at one time. "It means a lot to us."

"Of course," Fred said. "It's not a problem at all. We want to accommodate everyone who wants to be there. You can head in whenever you are ready."

Lana motioned to her siblings to follow Fred into the unit, but she stayed behind so that she could walk in with Sara, whom she knew was lingering towards the back of the crowd.

"You ok, Sara?" Lana said once it was just the two of them.

"No," Sara said.

"I know this is tough, but she isn't going to get better. You know that, right?" Lana said.

"Yeah," Sara said, staring at the floor.

"Are you going to be able to go through with this?" Lana asked.

"No," Sara said, her words monotone and staccato.

"I can't say the words, Lana. I can't say that I want to take her off life support. I won't say it!" Sara said bursting into tears.

"You don't have to, Sis. I will say it. I just need to know that you won't hate me for it," Lana said, hugging her little sister.

"No, I don't hate you!" Sara said, laughing through her tears.

"Come on, then. Let's go," Lana said, pulling Sara towards the door. "You don't have to say anything at all."

Chelsea had never seen so many people crammed into one room in her life. It felt like a cartoon, in a way, with people piled on top of one another and spilling out into the main unit. She herself stood outside the room, by the nursing station. Fred was in the room, and there only needed to be one physician in the room for the withdraw. Chelsea stayed outside, but could see the crowd through the glass window.

Inside, Lana and Sara were at the head of the bed with Fred and the respiratory therapist. Victoria's nurse had hung a morphine drip several minutes earlier and the medication was permeating in Victoria's veins by now. She hadn't seemed to be in pain without the morphine drip, but it was standard to have it going, just in case. The room was quiet except for the sobs and the sounds of the monitors and machines.

Fred nodded to the respiratory technician who unstrapped the collar that held the ventilator tube in place. As he loosened the chinstrap, they could see the indentations remaining in Victoria's chin. With one slow and steady motion, he pulled the tube lightly until it was entirely out of Victoria's mouth. Loud alarms erupted from the ventilator box as it detected that the tube had come out. The technician reached over quickly to silence it. He then took a suction catheter and cleared the saliva that had pooled in her mouth. Once the tube was out, Victoria's jaw closed gently for the first time since she had been intubated. She was breathing in tiny, shallow breaths. Her eyes remained closed and her body was still. Fred was relieved that there was no sudden gasp for air, which happens occasionally during an extubation. It is something that usually upsets the family, but Victoria didn't gasp. She was peaceful and serene.

For Lana, she was seeing her mother the way she remembered her. Her mouth closed, no tubes jutting out. She was as close to the mother that she knew as was possible. Instead of the sounds of the ventilator, the soft whispers of prayers permeated from the crowd in the room and the family stood together with Victoria as her breathing slowed.

Outside, Chelsea wondered how long it would take. She had performed many withdraws and was amazed at how different each one could be. Some patients linger for hours after the ventilator is withdrawn. They are able to breath on their own for a few hours, but eventually, the strength that allowed them to maintain their oxygen levels fades and they succumb to a respiratory fatigue. Others go right away, they simply cannot survive for any length of time without the ventilator. Chelsea wondered what Victoria's body would do and then wondered which way would be *best*. Although its easier for the family if the patient dies right away so they don't have to stand by and watch a long and drawn out decline. However, when it happens right after the ventilator is withdrawn, it can worsen feelings of guilt because the family sees a direct relation to *their* decision to take out the tube and the death of their loved one. Chelsea sometimes thought it was better if the two events were spaced out in time, but you could never be sure how any family will react to the passing of loved one. It always seemed to be a little easier when the family had some time with their loved one after they were 'unveiled' from the shroud of the ventilator. Chelsea hoped Victoria could breathe on her own long enough for all forty of her family members to say their goodbyes in their own time.

Victoria passed away within twenty minutes. As her shallow breaths could not sustain her oxygen levels, her heart eventually slowed and ceased to beat. Her death was gentle and peaceful and her final moments were spent surrounded by the ones who loved her most. She felt no pain and her family stood on as a unit as they said their goodbyes. There was no CPR, no drama, simply peace. Victoria's death was neat and organized, just like the home that she kept. There was no chaos or uncertainty, but instead there were prayers and love.

Lana and Sara were the last in the room after the nurse switched off the monitor. At the time her heart had stopped, they had all seen it on the monitor and Fred had gone inside the room to declare Victoria deceased. As the family trickled out one by one, Chelsea waited in the nursing station, hoping for a moment to say goodbye to Lana. She reflected on her first meeting with Victoria, and remembered her calm eyes and how they had reminded her of her own mother. She recalled how important it had been for her to 'get it right' with Victoria's care. Looking back on the whole experience, Chelsea knew that they had. Victoria's death had matched her personality, calm and contained. They had enabled her entire family to be at her bedside and controlled the situation enough so that everyone could be at peace.

Sara left the room, her face streaked with tears, and Lana came out a few seconds behind her. She saw Fred was in the room across the way, speaking with the family member of another patient. Her eyes searched for Chelsea and she found her sitting in the nursing station. She approached her with a smile.

"Thank you for everything," Lana said.

"You are most welcome," Chelsea said. "I'm so sorry we couldn't do more. Your mother was a very brave woman."

Lana sniffed and nodded but did not cry. Her eyes were so calm and steady, it was almost haunting to Chelsea.

"Take care," Chelsea said.

"I will," Lana said. As she turned to leave, she took one last look at Chelsea and at the unit. With a nod to herself, she pushed through the door without looking back.

Resource Section

Now that you've read the stories within *DNR*, you have had exposure to some of the more common medical interventions and decisions that you or your loved one may someday face. Most of the patients and their families that I've met through my work have not been exposed to any of these topics and it is my hope that reading the stories of these patients and their families has given you an advantage and insight into the world within the intensive care unit. Each story was chosen to demonstrate a specific concept, whether that is what CPR is truly like, what being on a breathing machine entails, what it's like to remove someone from life support or the possible benefits of hospice care. Although at times, *DNR* is admittedly tough to read, I hope that you have formed opinions and preferences about how you envision your own medical care to proceed should you become critically ill, whether that be full, aggressive care or one that is aimed more at comfort than cure.

Using these opinions, I encourage you to plan ahead and think about the topics and concepts presented in *DNR*. An excellent way to begin this process is to complete an advance directive and name someone you know and trust as your surrogate decision maker (your power of attorney). What follows is a discussion about the times when these documents are helpful, and even more importantly, the times when they are not. Misconceptions of advance directives abound amongst doctors and patients alike, and it is my hope that this section can be used as a tool to provide some much-needed clarification.

Advance Directives: Even Doctors Get It Wrong

My first real lesson in advance directives snuck up on me when I was least expecting it. It was my second week in the intensive care unit and my white coat was still pristinely white and freshly pressed. I heard a nurse yell for assistance and upon entering the patient's room found myself in the precarious position of being the first doctor in the room for a cardiac arrest. As the nurse was scrambling for the oxygen mask, I started CPR. After a few minutes the rest of the code team came crashing into the room, the patient was intubated and started on pressors to raise the blood pressure. Once the patient's doctor arrived, he told us that the patient was seventy years old, never sick a day in his life, and had come in to the hospital with a pneumonia.

It wasn't very long before we had gotten back the pulse and the blood pressure. The patient was saved. As we stood around the patient's bedside, watching the monitor, a nurse came into the room hysterically waving a piece of paper. It was the patient's advance directive. On it was a checklist where the patient had checked off that he did not want CPR or mechanical ventilation. I remember how my heart dropped when I saw that paper. I had been the first to start CPR, and the thought never even occurred to me to even ask if the patient was a full code. I had just started the compressions.

I backed out of the room, my presence not missed amongst the swarms of more senior doctors who had since flooded the room since I had started the CPR. I welled up with tears feeling horrified that I had done the wrong thing. I had started a code on a patient who was DNR. I ran down six flights of stairs to visit my mentor, Dr. Poe, choking back tears and plopped myself down onto my favorite chair in his office, one I would come to know often through the years.

Through my sobs I told him what had happened and what I had done, but he just shook his head and grinned.

"Did you actually read the advance directive?" he asked me.

"Well, yeah," I told him, "He checked off that he didn't want CPR or intubation. "

"Did you read the statements before that?"

I didn't know what he was talking about so I just kept right on crying, feeling terrible for my negligence. Once he calmed me down, he explained to me that I had in fact, done the right thing.

"This is exactly why I don't have an advance directive," he said. "No one understands them. And this is a perfect example. You're a doctor and the advance directive confused you. From what you've told me, LJ, his advance directive doesn't apply. You did the right thing by saving him."

And he was right. I had done the right thing by starting the CPR and he ended up walking out of the hospital just a few weeks later. Thankfully, the nurse brought in the advance directive *after* I had started the CPR. The confusion, and importantly, the lesson, is all about those first few statements, the ones no one ever reads or understands.

The Advance Directive Checklist: yes/no....maybe

Unfortunately, even the most well-intentioned advance directive may be written in such a way that it can be incredibly difficult to interpret. Even just the layout of the document can lead to a misinterpretation of what's written. And obviously, when dealing with life and death, there is no room for misinterpretation. Below is an example of a commonly seen version of an advance directive, in fact, the same version of an advance directive that sent me weeping to Dr. Poe's office.

DECLARATION

I, _____, being of sound mind, willfully and voluntarily make this declaration to be followed if I become incompetent. This declaration reflects my firm and settled commitment to refuse life-sustaining treatment under the circumstances indicated below.

I direct my attending physician to withhold or withdraw life-sustaining treatment that serves only to prolong the process of my dying, if I should be in a terminal condition or in a state of permanent unconsciousness.

I direct that treatment be limited to measures to keep me comfortable and to relieve pain, including any pain that might occur by withholding or withdrawing life-sustaining treatment.

In addition, if I am in the condition described above, I feel especially strongly about the following forms of treatment:

I ( )do ( )do not want cardiac resuscitation.

I ( )do ( )do not want mechanical respiration.

I ( )do ( )do not want tube feeding or any other artificial or invasive form of nutrition (food) or hydration (water).

I ( )do ( )do not want blood or blood products.

I ( )do ( )do not want any form of surgery or invasive diagnostic tests.

I ( )do ( )do not want kidney dialysis.

I ( )do ( )do not want antibiotics.

I realize that if I do not specifically indicate my preference regarding any of the forms of treatment listed previously, I may receive that form of treatment.

The checklist draws our eyes immediately to the "Do/Do Not want" options. This can lead to inadvertently ignoring the most critical statement of all, the clause that lays out the condition in which the advance directive would take effect:

"I direct my attending physician to withhold or withdraw life-sustaining treatment that serves only to prolong the process of my dying, *if I should be in a terminal condition or in a state of permanent unconsciousness.*"

Let's take for example two extremes to illustrate the importance of this statement. First, imagine that you were stung by a bee and had a terrible allergic reaction. You're otherwise healthy and perfectly fine, but terribly allergic to bees. By the time you make it to the emergency room your throat has swollen up and you suddenly can't breathe. The bee sting caused the swelling, which can be controlled and reversed by intravenous steroids and other medications, but these medications may take some time to work. The doctors need to put you on a ventilator or else you will die. You have a reversible condition requiring life support. Under this circumstance, the above advance directive doesn't apply.

This is crucial to understand: having an advance directive where you've checked off the box saying you would not want life support *does not mean* that you won't end up getting CPR or being put on a breathing machine if it is thought that your condition may be reversible. There are certainly times when CPR or brief periods on life support can be life saving and beneficial and advance directives are written in such a way to account for these situations, such as the bee sting. However, if your preference is to never, under any circumstances be put on life support, then this must be clearly specified in an advance directive and the wording of the generic advance directive would have to be changed.

Now let's look at the other extreme, for example, a patient like Victoria whose terminal lung cancer caused her to develop shortness of breath so severe she required the ventilator in order to maintain her oxygen levels. She did not have an advance directive, and even though she had an irreversible condition, she was placed on life support. Had Victoria possessed an advance directive saying she would not want to be placed on a ventilator if she had an irreversible disease, she may have avoided being placed on the ventilator at the time of her respiratory de-compensation, had that been her wish. Instead, the doctors would have transitioned her care to palliative measures or hospice care, with an emphasis on administering medications to reduce her pain, discomfort and shortness of breath. When the decision about life support needed to be made emergently, Victoria was under too much duress to think clearly and make any decisions about her wishes, relying on Lana, her daughter, to make a decision without knowing what her mom may have wanted.

In situations like these, the advance directive may take some the guesswork and decision making burden away from family members in emergent situations where clear thinking is seemingly impossible. It also may have helped Sara, Victoria's youngest daughter as she struggled with the final decision to remove Victoria from the ventilator. Perhaps an advance directive may have helped Sara come to terms with the ultimate decision to withdraw life support had she known it was truly her mother's own wish as documented in her advance directive.

Similarly, the drama, tension and conflict that surrounded Mrs. Chandler's care may have been minimized by an advance directive. For Mrs. Chandler, the physicians felt that pressing on was inhumane, yet her family felt that Mrs. Chandler would have wanted every possible intervention to prolong her life, regardless of the state she was in. Missing from the whole dynamic was the voice of Mrs. Chandler. An advance directive may have confirmed her wishes, and perhaps confirmed that she *did* in fact want fully aggressive care. This could have alleviated much of the angst and tension between the medical team and the family and leading to better quality of care for Mrs. Chandler.

Advance Directives: Helpful to a point

Advance directives can be incredibly useful when helping make decisions about what to do for a patient with a well-defined condition, like the bee sting or the end stage lung cancer. However, try as we might to plan ahead for the end of life, the stark reality of it all is that decisions come up that we did not foresee. Our bodies are unpredictable, and unfortunately so are the ways in which they will break down. Inevitably, there will be times when the advance directive can't predict a medical scenario that may present itself. There may be reversible processes superimposed on terminal conditions, for example, a devastating pneumonia in a patient with breast cancer. The breast cancer itself may not be the cause of the patient's deterioration, but the presence of the cancer makes it such that the body cannot fight the infection. What would the checklist say about this situation?

We can look to Bruce's story as an example. When I first met him as an intern, his disease was close to the point of irreversibility. His infection was so severe there was a good chance he would not have pulled through. He was on life support for a prolonged period of time and endured tremendous suffering. His disease could have taken his life at any point and it certainly would not have been unreasonable to transition his care to comfort measures or hospice care. But his doctors and family pressed on, knowing that infections, even as bad as his, *may* eventually be reversible. Bruce's story demonstrates the element of grey. He had a potentially reversible infection overlaying a terminal condition (his severe heart failure) since, at the time, Bruce was not a transplant candidate because of his infection, and his heart failure was irreversible in the absence of a transplant. Had Bruce possessed an advance directive saying with a check mark that he did not want mechanical ventilation, would it have applied in this circumstance? It's not so cut and dry as a simple yes/no answer and this demonstrates again how the checkbox advance directive may fail.

After all, end of life decision-making is not about yes/no answers. It's about judgment and scenarios, it's about taking the full picture into consideration and making the best decision possible based on the information we have and what we know about what the patient would want to endure. This is why the advance directive cannot stand as an entity by itself; it cannot exhibit judgment on its own.

Enter the surrogate decision maker.

Surrogate Decision Makers: Naming your Go-To Person

Regardless of whether you have an advance directive or not, if you become unable to make your own medical decisions, your medical team should seek out your family for guidance in making decisions for your medical care. Even when an advance directive has been filled out, physicians should not make medical decisions for an incapacitated patient in the absence of consultation with the patients' family. This means, however, that someone will carry the heavy responsibility of speaking for you and helping the doctors to uphold your wishes if you become unable to communicate with your medical team.

Despite the peppering of different terms that exist for this person (health care proxy, power of attorney, surrogate decision maker, next of kin), they all basically mean the same thing: who is going to be the "go-to" person for the medical team? Choosing this person is probably the most important thing you can specify when considering end of life planning and is arguably the best way to maintain control and prevent conflict or uncertainty. This decision shouldn't be made lightly and a lot of different considerations need to go into choosing your decision maker. This person will literally have your life in their hands.

First, however, let's consider what might happen in the absence of an officially named surrogate decision maker. The default "go-to" person is the legal next of kin, usually the spouse or eldest child, depending on state laws. Most advance directives and living wills have a section in which you can name a power of attorney, who may or may not be the same person as your legal next of kin. This designation is usually found after the checklist:

I ( )do ( )do not want to designate another person as my surrogate to make medical treatment decisions for me if I should be incompetent and in a terminal condition or in a state of permanent unconsciousness.

Name and address of surrogate (if applicable):

_____

Name and address of substitute surrogate (if surrogate designated above is unable to serve): _____

I made this declaration on the_____day of _____(month, year).

Declarant's signature:

_____

Declarant's address:

_____

The declarant or the person on behalf of and at the direction of the declarant knowingly and voluntarily signed this writing by signature or mark in my presence.

Witness' signature:

_____

Witness' address:

_____

Witness' signature:

_____

Witness' address:

_____

When you name a power of attorney in an advance directive, this designated person's decisions will trump those of the next of kin. So, for example, if you wish to have your best friend make your medical decisions for you rather than your child, you would need to have your friend named as your power of attorney in a legal document.

As long as you've named your "go-to" person in writing, there should not be any doubt about who will be in control of your medical decisions. Theoretically. However, reality and theory often do not coincide. It's equally important to tell your family who the decision maker will be to avoid any surprises when a crisis arises. Surprises are never good in the world of intensive care, and having family members fight and disagree over who will make the final decisions is all too common. Who you've chosen to be your go to person should be clearly communicated to your family, preferably in a time of health. This way, if there is disagreement it can be discussed in a non-emergent setting as opposed to the intensive care unit. Even the most closely knit families may disagree and even though you may hope everyone in your family will come together in a time of crisis, that, unfortunately, is not always the case. Unifying your family behind a single person beforehand will help the doctors take better care of you and also to help your loved ones through a time of crisis when you may not be able to help them otherwise.

Upholding Your Wishes: Your philosophy.

Being someone's medical decision maker is a tough job under any circumstance, particularly when faced with decisions about continuing with aggressive medical care or transitioning care to comfort measures only. It can be agonizing, particularly if your go-to person is not prepared to make the tough choices that will inevitably arise. An unprepared surrogate decision maker is almost as unhelpful as no decision maker at all. Granted, there is no way to predict what situation may arise, but we can make decisions ahead of time about our overall philosophy on end of life care. Just as there are countless variants of religious and moral beliefs in our society, so are there countless variants of how you might feel about the way your body is treated in a time of critical illness and impending death.

In order to appropriately prepare your go-to person for the decisions that lay ahead, you have to know for yourself what you would want under certain general circumstances. After all, how can you possibly expect someone else to figure out what you would want if you don't know for yourself? Its not pleasant to think about our own demise or what might happen if we suddenly became critically ill, but ignoring our own mortality will only make matters even more uncertain. Although it seems daunting, its important to define your overall philosophy and your general gestalt about what kinds of medical care you prefer.

Do this by thinking about what's important to you and talk about it with your decision maker. Talk about how you feel about independence, about hospitals, about doctors, about awareness, about death, about organ donation. What matters to you? What does quality of life mean to you and at what cost are you willing to preserve your bodily functions? Would you be agreeable to being fed by a tube in order to stay alive? Would you be agreeable to being unconscious on a ventilator if it meant you were able to keep fighting another day? How long would you allow your body to be maintained on life support before wanting to succumb or would you want to hold on to life at all costs?

As a unique example, take Patrick, the teenager who, after a lifetime of being a slave to cystic fibrosis, was able to gain control and peace in his final months. Those who knew Patrick knew that his decision to stop aggressive treatment and enroll in hospice care, even at the young age of 19, was in line with the way that he desired his life to be: independent of nebulizers, cystic fibrosis medications and machines. Once he was diagnosed with the dreaded superbug, *Cepacia*, he reached a turning point in his life in which he was able to regain control and live out the rest of his life on his own terms, based on his definition of quality of life. His overall philosophy of life was not one which would tolerate his final months being spent amidst doctors, hospitals and isolation rooms. To his family and friends who had observed Patrick's lifelong struggle for normality, his choice seemed obvious. Because Patrick was able to successfully define his philosophy of quality of life and to set clear boundaries for his medical care, his final months were spent exactly as he envisioned.

With medical decision-making, there is no absolute right or wrong answer, only what is right or wrong for you. Families often ask me "what is the right thing to do, doctor," a question to which I have no answer other than "there is no one right thing, only what is right for your loved one." It's a nebulous response and certainly hard to hear when faced with trying to pontificate on what your ill loved one might want or expect you to do. Taking *most* of the guess work out of the equation can be achieved, but only if you talk to your decision maker, loved ones and doctors about your general philosophy. Your discussion will build the foundation they will need to make your decisions. Without it, your decision makers will be left without your voice to make tough choices, which, without the appropriate level of preparedness may be even more difficult and painful than the grief of losing a loved one.

Where to Go for More Information

DNR is by no means a comprehensive guide to end of life care and planning. I encourage you to use DNR as a tool to begin thinking about the above concepts and principles, and to spend some time reflecting on the way these stories made you feel and the opinions you formed as you read the experiences of these five patients. Talk to your loved ones and family about your reflections and try to open a discussion about these topics we tend to avoid. Prepare yourself, prepare your doctors and prepare your family with the tools they'll need to carry through your wishes and your legacy.

Visit www.DNRstories.com for discussion boards and information and resources about DNR and medical decision-making.

Acknowledgements

DNR could not have been written without the help, support and encouragement of my mentors, family and friends. From the conception of this project to the implementation, I have been blessed with a strong network surrounding me that has enabled *DNR* to take shape.

DNR would not exist if it weren't for Dr. Jill Bolte Taylor, whose response to a simple email made a project that seemed like a pipe dream become a possibility. I am also thankful for the work of Ms. Ellen Stiefler of Transmedia Agency for taking me under her wing and guiding me through the world of publishing.

I am especially grateful for the mentorship and friendship of Dr. Michael Sherman and Dr. Richard Paluzzi- not only for their guidance throughout this project and my career thus far, but also through life. I'm also grateful for the countless other faculty, nurses, case managers and friends I've made at Drexel University College of Medicine and Hahnemann Hospital.

Thanks go to the physicians, patients, nurses and family members who granted me interviews to ensure the accuracy of this work as well as to help me capture the color of the people who make up the stories of DNR.

I'd also like to thank my entire family, from my husband, Mike, to my amazingly supportive parents, Michael Pitkow and Barbara Healy, as well as my wonderful stepparents, Tim Healy and Jane Schreiber. Thanks go to my brothers Xaq and Sam Pitkow and all of my very special in-laws. A special thank you goes to my dad for his work on editing, design, website and overall encouragement and to my brother Xaq for his editing and design expertise.

Lastly, I'd like to thank my patients and their families, past, present and future for the honor of treating them through their struggles and victories.

DNR • Do Not Resuscitate

LaVergne, TN USA
03 April 2011
222581LV00002B/2/P